Praise for
Just One Conscious Breath

Reader be advised. Michael is about to take you on a Camino, a spiritual pilgrimage to the 'holy grail' of your inner peace. As a master storyteller and student of numerous wisdom traditions, he weaves a narrative combining his many years of teaching neurodivergent children and living in a multicultural setting. Though vastly informative and entertaining, the true crux of what he shares comes through the adept unpacking of the treasures of the breath. Though I have been a student and teacher of breathwork for some fifty years, I was taken deeper with the exercises Michael presented at the end of each chapter into my understanding and wonder of the miraculous teacher right under my nose in *Just One Conscious Breath*.

– Jim Morningstar, PhD
Director, Therapeutic Breathwork Training Program
Co-director, Global Professional Breathwork Alliance

With *Just One Conscious Breath*, Michael Wood brings us into the universality of energetic presence that is available to us all. His melodic process of guiding us on the path of the breath is enchanting, trance-like, and unique in and of itself. His gentle guidance leads us through story and exercises, helping the reader build a profoundly kind relationship with parts of ourselves we never knew could heal through this infinitely abundant nourishment. Through sound, awakening, ego, anger, flow and emanation, Michael leads us time and time again together with the soft prompt: 'Let's breathe'. And at once we are brought into the surrender, the silence, and the reconstruction of life and the self through an inherited treasure that is ultimately grounded in accountability, authenticity, love and unity afforded by one conscious breath.

– Claudia de Llano, MFT,
Author of *The Seven Destinies of Love*

Just One
Conscious Breath

The profoundly simple practice
that moves you from reaction
to response

Michael Wood

A Pilgrimbreath Press Book

First published by Pilgrimbreath Press in 2024

For more information about Michael Wood, visit: PilgrimBreath.org

Cover design by Martin Publishing Services
Dolphin illustration by Hafizh Hafrildo
Zen circle illustration by Elinacious on DepositPhotos.com
'Weary Pilgrim' by Bob Quinn; printed with kind permission from Dermot Kelly
Editing by Room 206: Writing
Interior design and proofreading by Liz Pond

The ideas and suggestions shared in this book are not intended as a substitute for advice from a healthcare professional. Please seek professional guidance on all matters concerning your health.

The author has made every effort to ensure all internet addresses are accurate at the time of publication. The third-party websites mentioned in this book are under the responsibility and control of the parties who have published them; the author assumes no responsibility for any content published on third-party websites.

Print (paperback): 978-1-0687466-0-4
E-book: 978-1-0687466-1-1

With love and gratitude to:

Binnie and Jim, my breath workers.
The children of Saplings School in Dublin.
Danusia and Luke for their love and deep intuition.
Beryl Ann (1931–2023), granddaughter of Bertie Buckland.

Human freedom involves our capacity to pause between stimulus and response and, in that pause, to choose the one response toward which we wish to throw our weight.

– Rollo May

Contents

Foreword

What is a foreword? I'm not sure there is a template. What is certain is that it is the first word, and I have been offered the inestimable privilege of uttering it, as it were, *ex nihilo*. The only word I feel qualified to offer, which could possibly be helpful for you as you prepare to entrust yourself to Michael's company, is a word of authentication.

Michael and I have been walking the Camino of life together for over 40 years; sometimes in lockstep, often just a few paces apart. For a while, Michael disappeared over the horizon as he underwent a process of radical spiritual catharsis and realignment, but we caught up with one another, as pilgrims do.

We met as fellow students and soon the roots of our friendship were well established, aided and abetted by copious quantities of real ale (a passion of Michael's at the time) and, it seemed, endless opportunities to converse spaciously about matters both profound and prosaic. If we weren't in the bar, we were in the kitchen, where Michael would produce endless cups of coffee from his much-coveted coffee machine.

At that time, Michael, 18, was shackled by what he describes in these pages as his 'socially conditioned life'. He was on track to make his life offering at the shrine of 21st century corporate capitalism – the destiny his suburban English formation had allotted.

But that was always going to be the road to nowhere for Michael. My father, a man of crystalline integrity and shrewd appreciation of character, was completely bemused by the thought that the Michael he knew to be a young man of rare generosity, perceptiveness and kindness would be content with a life marketing cosmetics or cars or whatever else paid him top dollar.

As you will read, Michael's Camino has been a journey of unbinding, of discovering the truth which has set him free, which has the potential to set us all free, via one conscious breath.

What follows is a gift which defies easy description. Three golden threads, tightly woven. One, Michael's own spiritual journey, recounted with luminous self-awareness, honesty and humour. Two, the sharing of wisdom: wisdom from diverse spiritual teachers and traditions, and perhaps, most movingly, from the neurodiverse community which Michael led as principal; wisdom illuminating the stuff of everyday life, the challenges that Every(wo)man has to find a way through; and wisdom relayed with the teacher's gift for apt illustration and anecdote. And three, a commendation of breathwork as the key to our own awakening and the liberation of our true potential.

These golden threads, woven with passion, generosity and love, comprise a gift which, if you surrender to it, *inspire it*, has the potential to be life-changing. What I know without qualification is that in Michael, you have the surest, most trustworthy, most authentic guide and companion.

– **Clive Gregory (former Bishop of Wolverhampton)**

Preface

Our pens may be disposable, but our life force can never run dry. Our case has a finite existence, and when we let it, the ink flows and flows.

I am writing with an old Bic pen, with a clear plastic case, a coloured stopper, and a slowly receding line of ink. My grandfather remembered when ballpoint pens were invented. He was a tailor and welcomed being able to mark up the valuable fitting sheet without the fear of ink splodges and to make notes on the train going into work. He said it cost him a day's wages – an arm and a leg – to buy one. These pens became such a visible source of my study and work life.

Although the pens are disposable, I have never used one up in all these years. Has anyone? Where do they all go? I have mine on an old school table, the kind my grandfather may have sat at. The line of black ink has now vanished, but the pen writes on, drawing on unseen reserves below the nib. Finishing this pen will literally be a first for me after more than forty years. That's just the life cycle of a disposable pen. Everything we consume has a life before it becomes our rubbish; temporary assets pausing on their way to landfill.

I work closely with a wonderful social enterprise called ReCreate Ireland, a small warehouse on the edge of an industrial estate on the edge of Dublin. They are the penultimate link in the chain of waste, and they carefully store and stock old items thrown out from the manufacturing process which are then reimagined into something new and creative, and reused by local community groups. Art displays frequently change to inspire members to see just what is possible when we let go of the limitations that we put on the everyday everything.

In these days of hyperanalysis at the touch of a button, the deepest thing we can teach students is to understand and access their authentic and creative reserves. This empowers them to be free to get on with it themselves. At its deepest level, education is about helping people connect with their authentic selves, to wake up to themselves. Once we access our being, the creative tap is turned on and we almost have no choice in the matter but to create.

I want you to see breathing as creative, by tapping into what we have and seeing it in a completely new and fresh way. Did you know that the word 'inspire' derives its source from the Latin word *inspirare*, which means 'to breathe into'? And so, this is why. This is why I sit here with my Bic pen and I write to you – because I didn't know any of this either. Until I did.

I have detoured a lot, sometimes taking the scenic route and many one-way streets off it. I started working in marketing in London and had a few different roles. For the last twenty-five years, I worked in many aspects of special education across Ireland, winding up in a school for children with autism and complex needs. On the way, I became a gardener, spiritual companion, teacher of presence and breath worker. But that's just stuff, I am just Michael, another bozo on the bus. I am just like you, and you are just like me. I discovered a new place along the way, one which I had never really been to before, and it kind of changed me, improved me, made me put down the pint and choose something different. Something more. That place is called *here*. Right here. Here in the now. Here with me. Here with you.

As we consciously start to wake up to our breath, we enter a free zone of limitless creativity. As we consciously breathe, we open. We open and we love. We love and we let go. We let go and we see. We see, and we understand. And then we wheel around again and again.

In awakening, we have a new way of seeing all our stuff and mess. We awaken to our limitless creativity. We discover our deepest and most authentic level of self. In breathing we can access the truest expression of ourselves. We meet our oneness, or our emptiness, and know of the core of love that unites everything.

As we awaken, we awaken to the infinite potential that we are, and this breathes inspiration and creativity into every aspect of our work and life. To some extent, I've experienced this for myself, and I am here to share with you what I know, and what I am still learning, so that we can learn together. So that no matter the hardship, the hang-up or the despair, we go again tomorrow.

Incidentally, my Bic pen literally ran out on completing this section, in the first draft of this book. That morning, I was on a walk in the local park when I glanced down and there was a brand-new Bic pen, resting on the path for me, in a different colour.

Introduction

I Surface and Exhale

This is not the exhale of despair or resignation as is often understood. This is the exhale of surrender, of letting go. It's the relaxed sound of our soul.

Dear Reader

I want this to be simple. I trust in simplicity, and I have learned my most profound lessons this way and will try to write to you from here. I want you to forget everything you know about breathing and stop thinking for a while (although to be honest with you, this book is largely about the complexity of that request). I want you to do nothing but take a pilgrim journey with me through these bite-size chapters. Mostly, I want you to live a better life. A richer, more satisfying, less dramatic, more celebratory life – without thinking you have to sell your soul, or pay for group therapy sessions, or lie on a yoga mat for hours hoping the light will come. This is not that.

So, what is it, then? I am a regular practical person. I'm certainly no monk who sold his Ferrari. I overthink, I break stuff, I mess up, I build back, sometimes better – I recall lying on a yoga mat in my thirties, thinking this is 'just not for me'. Up to my forties, getting in touch with 'feelings' was best done by other people elsewhere. And then there's my mother, and my mother's grandfather, Bertie Buckland. Bertie was the chief Druid who celebrated the summer solstice at Stonehenge in 1925, back in the day when they were allowed access to the stones. I never met him, but Mum was very proud and saw a deep connection early on and, at every opportunity, soldered us together with stories and memories. And so I guess there was curiosity hidden inside me all along.

I surface and exhale.

I completed a course in awakening, and I kind of got *there* – you know, to that place we're all looking for – but then I kind of didn't. This was because the learning was all in my head. It wasn't yet my experience, and it wasn't fully embodied. There was something missing, something more that I needed. I undertook some breathwork and did a series of ten conscious connected breathwork sessions. This is also known as rebirthing or source breathwork. There was no big flash of awakening here either. Appropriately perhaps, given my English nature, it was all somewhat incremental, cautious and undramatic. It wasn't sudden or earth-shattering; there were no big tears or drama. It just floated into being quietly, almost unnoticed. It was more like an apologetic slippery slope to awakening.

For me, *there* only slipped in in my fifties, and only when I was in complete surrender to flow. Appropriately I was on a barge with my breath worker, floating on the River Thames just a couple of miles upstream from where I was born over fifty-five years earlier. It just kind of happened. More of this I'll explain later.

I have plodded through life taking the fork in the open road when it 'felt' right. Being vulnerable has never been my strong suit. In writing this though, many years later, know this: I am not your teacher. I am a fellow pilgrim of the breath, and we are breathing this way together. I've learned so much about myself through my breath. My hope is that in sharing this, you will too.

I surface and exhale.

I call this opening of our journey *The Waking Breath*. This waking breath enables us to be in the heart. To be here and to be from it. Getting out of our heads and living in the heart is both our journey and our destination. When I am unsure – which is increasingly often – I trust this breath to help me out. To help me let go. What this most means for me is to let go of my identification with thoughts and return to my heart. And writing this way is the same thing; letting go of the identification with what's in my head, while holding onto the pen. This has been hard for me, writing my first book. I will share with you what brought me here, at the risk of feeling too vulnerable: I've been told I owe you this, my reader. Something I was not prepared for – but how can we express ourselves without surrendering to our learning? I understand this now.

Through experiences in my own life, I will share the techniques I have come to learn at the end of most chapters – for you to breathe, learn, live deeper. Use this book, not as a book but rather as a possible map shared by a fellow pilgrim for the Way. A daily compass for your lungs, and a north star for guidance.

Throughout this book you will have breathing space. A chance to reflect on the stories and teachings and then practise a corresponding breath. Sometimes, we merely reflect, jot down notes, or hold space for introspective thoughts. I encourage you to turn to these pages daily; a chapter a day would be good. Simply tap in as you go, and watch the breath as you consciously inhale, and let go on the exhale. There's nothing more to do here than surface, breathe, and wake up. If you already know this to be true, close the book, jump ship, and swim to the shore. If, on the other hand, you are curious – or you simply wish to renew your breath and open your truth – stay on board for a while.

I surface and exhale.

Just one conscious breath has supported me. You don't need expensive lessons or to hop on a plane to Bali to 'figure stuff out'. You just need to breathe consciously and let go. You can do it with me here in faith because when we become simple, our path does too.

I will be there … until *you* get there.

Your fellow pilgrim, on the exhale.

Michael

Part 1

Breathe

Between the pages before you there lay many more conscious breaths that will let you be, and take up space, in a healthy, joyful, self-appreciating kind of way.

Think of it like this: every conscious breath is a love letter to the body. It's short and sweet, and sacred. It brings you into your heart. Use these conscious breaths to relax you, clear you, inform you – at home, at work, at play. Teach it to yourself, teach it to your family, teach it to your colleagues. Our one conscious breath is going to evolve and deepen as we progress through the book.

Sometimes the greatest answers come from asking no questions at all.

Chapter 1

The Sound
of Your Breath

What does breath sound like?

It's an interesting question; one not many of us have probably asked. As we begin this journey, I encourage you to ask this question and explore the answers for yourself. Your breath is unique, and you'll soon learn how to hear it, feel it, accept it and befriend it. So, ask the question. Ask many questions. Observe and explore. Later on, you will see that having asked and understood, you will need to let go of all that. But for now just listen to yourself.

This is how we will get conscious. But first, observe the jazz singer. I was at a jazz concert last weekend. The singer was in her flow, and everyone appreciated her beautiful voice. This was even more apparent during her scat singing. 'Scat' is when a jazz singer doesn't use words and instead improvises by singing abstract sounds. She vocalises rather than verbalises. In scat the human voice can be appreciated in a way that is beyond words and it gives the listener the ability to lean into the melody and hear; free of the need to process language and the attachment to thought that lyrics might bring.

Next, observe the autistic child. I learned so much from them during my time working alongside them. At school, we had children who were nonspeaking and communicated in many ways. Some of them, for much of the time, were as they were, and emanated honesty and positivity from this place. Some had an enormous sense of play and fun, which they used to engage people. The positivity that they could radiate was so great that on these occasions, they would be surrounded by people. They were like young human magnets. What was the pull, though?

It was their smile. I'm not just talking about the smiles on their faces. It was their smiles within. The simple soul smile, the heart-centred smile. These smiles start from the inside; they produce light and expand the child's whole body, up through their eyes, reflecting truth and joy right back at you. This is not a learned smile; it's not a social smile. This is an authentic and uninhibited smile that is deeply transformative in the moment. There is no inner stuff dulling it. It is pure heart. I have experienced the positive impact of a smile like this. Colleagues were really moved when a child who visibly struggled to understand themselves and their sensory world smiled in this way – and enhanced their own joy. It's oftentimes difficult for the 'normal' functioning mind to explain, or express. But it's real. It's so real because it's beyond our mind and it's right there, from their heart. This smile is unshakeable. A bit like scat, it is beyond words. In its presence, we experience a micro-moment of joy. Everything is going to be okay. Everything. And so – here we have it – the courageous and authentic role models for my desire for a return to the simplicity of our heart.

Back to the breath. Cue your breath. Conscious breath is all this. It is a simple, soul smile and it is scat. It sounds like scat singing and feels like smiling. Both are pre-speaking cues and are among the most authentic and profound methods of communication that we can make. Smile and scat describe a meaning in a way that is far deeper than words: when our communication is solely guided by words, thoughts and information, we lose curiosity and play, and a deeper meaning is missed.

Krishnamurti reminds us that when we teach a child the name of a bird, they no longer see it or hear its song. When information becomes a substitute for essence, all curiosity is lost, and our lives are impoverished.

Can you remember the last time you were angry? Now try to remember the sound of your breath. Was that angry too? Maybe you heard it catch in your upper chest as you breathed fast and shallow. Hearing our breath brings awareness to it and enables us to do something about it.

I went for a walk with a friend of mine in the forest and he exclaimed at a sound we both heard, 'Oh yes, yes, I know that… I know it… it's the rhythmic tapping of a woodpecker.' We both smiled. He was right. Impressive perhaps, but how truly helpful is that if it brings us both back to identification and thought – and no longer the sound of the woodpecker? Try taking a walk in the forest with a companion and say nothing, but point in the direction of the sound. Observe the difference.

When we practise conscious breathing, we're no longer identifying with the act of breathing; we are making sounds nonverbally, and we begin to have a conversation with our breath. Here, we have a greater opportunity to communicate in a freer way. We communicate and emanate consciousness more powerfully. Human sounds like *ahh*, *wow*, *phew* and *hmmm* are really examples of breath onomatopoeia that convey emotions way beyond words. In breathing them we open up space in our mind and temporarily put the handbrake on the thought stream. This enables us to communicate in an authentic and uncluttered way.

Let's try this together. Say: *aww*.

Aww is the breath of inspiration. It's the 'awe' in 'awesome' that comes on an exhale as we let go. It is a sound of appreciation and joy. When looking into the pure, uncluttered eyes of a baby, we say *aww* rather than, 'That baby is so naturally beautiful; I am in a state of pure appreciation and joy.' Instead, we breathe a sound. Turn this into a breath practice. Breathe in, exhale, and make the sound, *aww*. Try this a few times and feel the changes in your body.

Say: *wow*.

Hear the vibrational feeling it makes. *Wow* is a beautiful sound. It can be said on either the inhale, as a sharp intake of air, or released on the exhale. Imagine it's a beautiful day, you are out for a walk, the cloud is lifting as you ascend the hill over the lake. As you climb, new horizons and vistas open. What do you do next? Do you say, 'I'm glad we put in all the effort to climb the hill and enjoy these lovely views,' or do you just pause and let go and say *wow*? Words can never match the breath sounds when expressing joy.

Try to breathe this one. *Wow*. Pause. How does your body feel now?

How about the sound *phew*?

Phew is often associated with a sigh, a sense of relief, or a release. Here's a scenario. You've arrived home and put the key in the lock and have a feeling that there might be something untoward inside. You slowly enter the house and realise it is just the cat. All is well. You may make a sound like *phew*. *Phew* often follows a breath hold, which can temporarily happen when we are stressed. It often rushes out like air from a balloon. Which is so much more direct and honest than adding more words to the situation.

Try this one: *phew*. Take a long and easy exhale. Repeat as often as you can and track how your body feels afterwards.

Up next: *hmm* – this is a lovely sound.

It is made on a long exhale with the mouth closed. A long exhale is about relaxation and letting go. People often say *hmm* when agreeing with someone. *Hmm* vibrates on the lips a little. It's a different kind of breath sound – and an affirmative sound of positive listening and rapport that translates as a nod towards the speaker to continue, in the knowledge that they are being heard and will not be interrupted.

Let us try: *hmm*. Feel the vibration on your lips. How does your body feel now?

Lastly, my favourite sound of all. That sound of the slow air release that accompanies a sigh. The sound that this book started with. The sound of letting go.

For me, a sigh is one of the most powerful affirmations we could choose to make. It says, I don't know what is going on here, but I am okay with it; I am at peace with it. I see it, and I want to let it go and let it all be.

Try a really big sigh with me now, however that may sound for you. Drop your shoulders: sigh. Repeat it a few times; a slow sigh followed by a rapid sigh. Pause.

I recommend you become conscious of your sigh – and sigh as often as you can. A sigh is nature's way of just letting go. When you feel a sigh, jump on it, turn it into a theatrical one and deepen the benefit of these wonderful breaths that are hardwired into our systems. Our breath knows best – let yours lead you.

⟲ Let's breathe

Breathing space	Just One Conscious Breath
Duration	12 seconds
Response	To set your north star
Best for	Regular practice, as often as you can
Outcome	To begin to awaken

Our one conscious breath is going to deepen as we move through the book. Each conscious breath technique has its own outcome and response, but all are applied for greater well-being. For now, let's start. This is nothing complicated.

Every conscious breath is a love letter to the body. It's short and sweet, and sacred. It takes us to our heart. The entry level version of this breath goes like this:

Sit up straight. Close your eyes. Take a deep inhale for five counts. Simply watch one breath as we consciously inhale. Hold your breath here for two counts. Let go for five counts on the exhale. Now, be in that peace and stillness after the breath. Wait in that stillness.

Breathe.

Chapter 2

Pink Camels

Pink camels.

When I say 'pink camels', what happens? You think about them. Right? The Cleveland Clinic says that the brain processes seventy thousand thoughts each day.[1] That's around one for every second we are awake. Rather like King Canute and the rising tide, nothing we do will stop the constant flow of our thoughts, nor the pink camels. Especially when we resist, as what we resist persists. Let's try that now. Please do not think about pink camels... How was that? More pink camels, right? You see, what we resist persists. This is because in trying, we reinforce thought by putting our attention there and so encourage more.

Like the carbonated bubbles that pop through to the surface of a glass of soda, we know if we agitate the glass we will just encourage more, but if we give it space and observe it, they will begin to slow, and with time and patience they will cease. Thoughts, like bubbles in the glass, will only slow if we do not interfere and just allow them to be neutral, in time giving them space to pop and stop.

Back to the pink camels. Consider you're the herder of a caravan of pink camels and your job is to bring them safely and profitably along the passage of an ancient trading route. In order to trade you will have to nurture your flock by:

· Training them
· Keeping them healthy
· Nurturing the young
· Keeping them focused and in line
· Knowing how to securely fasten their baskets
· Being mindful of sandstorms from every side
· Being up front modelling the journey and in its flow.

Remember, if during the route individual camels look back at where they have been or look up to where they are to go, they may stumble, and the thread with the caravan will be lost.

Think of your mind as the whole caravan with its camels, herders and cargo. Beyond the caravan of it all is your wisdom of the route, your inner guidance and your north star. Like the ancient caravan herders, we undemonstratively navigate our way through life when we step out of the mind and allow our innate and ancient guidance to get on with it.

But how do we do all this? Quite simply, with one conscious breath. By taking just one conscious breath we step out of the crazy caravan of our mind and give space for our inner guide to lead the way. But what is going on here? Well, when we breathe consciously, we bring attention and awareness to what we do naturally. We cannot consciously circulate blood or digest food, but we *can* consciously breathe. When we consciously do what can also take place unconsciously, we create a gap between our awareness and our thoughts. From that space, there is awareness on the outside looking in.

When we step out of our mind in this way and look back, what are we looking with – what's looking in? We can only observe mind with no-mind, with no-thing. We observe it with our being. With our

Buddha nature. We experience what is in the background. This is the energy of everything.

But where does this energy come from? That's the key question in all this. The energy source we are tracking back to here is consciousness, which is universal energy and the source of everything. On this human journey, consciousness manifests in our heart and is expressed as love. Through consciousness we can more clearly see what isn't. The caravan is more than the collective energy of individual camels in it. At a deeper level they are the collective energy of everything they share with the herders and with the energy of the Way. When we see this, we know of source energy and love.

The key with any letting go is not getting reattached. In the spaciousness of an exhale we just let go. Then let go, let go, and let go again and again. And again and again. However much you let go, you can always let go a little more, just as however much you exhale, you can always exhale a little more. Let go of all attachments, intentions, techniques – and camels.

When you let go of something as precious as awareness, you trust deeply, and from this place you can experience universal stillness and source energy. This is the source of love. Sensing this is more than enough; it doesn't matter if it happens or not – just accept, don't judge, and let go. Your experience will show up in your love.

So to return to our neglected caravan of pink camels: as the herder we train and listen to our flock. Then, as we move on, our first tentative steps on a trading route with a new herd are taken with complete sur-render and trust. We let go. When we let go from a point of awareness, we let go of everything and let go into the arms of the rhythm of life or the energy of the Way.

As we let go, we trust in our north star and flow with it. As the inner flows so does the outer. So, at this time our breath will be rounded and smooth, flowing with energy. This is our internal music, the sound of the source of our love. When we hear it, and know it, we are flowing with the source energy of life, and the glorious contradictory hotchpotch of the caravan of our own life is held and is heading home.

When we step outside of ourselves and look in, we get a fresh perspective on who we are and what our thoughts are. We are not our camels. We are the observer. Taking a conscious breath enables this perspective. It gives us the opportunity to stop and watch, and when we do this we become the herder of our own mind and start to see clearly.

Chapter 3
Gen H

Gen X, Gen Y, Gen Z, Gen Alpha – you know them all.

We're constantly being told about the characteristics of preceding and dominating generations – but who's speaking about Gen H? I am. This is the generation we are all part of. You, me and everyone else. The H generation is one we have grown into: it's the 'Hurry' generation. The quicker we move, the more we get done. The faster we respond, the more useful we are to our society. We rush, we sprint, we panic, we get stuff done – and the craziest part of all is we're proud of ourselves for it.

Here's what's wrong with Gen H: when we hurry, we are sending a clear message to our bodies that the future, which we can't appreciate or experience, is more significant than the present, which we can. In that way we lose out – we miss the *now*. We don't experience the journey, just the expectation of arrival. We are in a hurry because we are driven by the sense that there is something out there that is more important or better than being here now. Yet when we get there, we are not fully there because we are focused on our next thing to do, and the hamster wheel just keeps spinning.

Being in a hurry becomes a culture, a mindset and a broken circuit in our human characteristic. It breaks our breathing circuit too. We spend our days constantly missing out. When we're always in a hurry, we become like an eternal rubber ball rebounding from surface to surface without a pause, bouncing to a future we can never meet and rest in. When we give the moment now the full dignity it deserves, the next thing becomes the next now. It's like we rest in one bounce then we rest in another, so *there* is not something we should be pursuing. *Here* is. And the irony is that in the state of *here* there is nothing to pursue and there is nowhere to go. *Now* becomes a habit. But if *now* is not a habit, then hurry rushes into the void to fill it. And so we start a vicious cycle of adrenalised energy cycles and subsequent let down.

Remember the image from childhood of a donkey running after a carrot dangled twelve inches from its nose, teased by what is ahead, never able to enjoy what is just out of reach. It would have made no sense to the donkey that to suddenly stop running would mean the carrot would swing back its way. But with just one conscious breath we put the handbrake on; we enable ourselves to enjoy the carrot of now and break the neverending circuit of the chase.

When we are simple and uncluttered, we can open up inner space from preoccupations of the past or future, helping our mind to simplify and clear.[2] This way our body can bring us here now. The great Tao of life flows from here. When people go to Kenya on holiday, they are taught the most important lesson in Swahili: 'pole pole' or 'slowly slowly'.

One of the joys and frustrations of working with students who had not developed our sense of clock time was that we could be working across two separate time zones – theirs and ours. Their time was often doing a preferred activity, being here now, whereas our work-specified time was about scheduling curriculum and activities and breaks and buses into their day. They understood pole pole and were probably right deep down. They were more naturally available to the present moment, and because of the demands of the clock, we seemed to be trying to hurry them out of it.

It was always good to see new colleagues arrive and experience the opportunity that working with our students brought them. But an even greater joy was to see the old game, the old dynamic around time, play out and to watch some of the students use their charm and behaviour to get new staff to bend to their will. The dynamic, whether spoken or unspoken, explicit or implicit, was often played out this way:

'You and the timetable want me to be *there* now, but I want to be *here* now doing *this* now – so what are you going to do about it?'

For some students it was enough that *they* knew that *you* knew the game was being played and so you both connected to the truth of that. With these students, once you had shared a laugh and acknowledged the game, the point of it all had been achieved and we were all free to move on. In these moments of deep connection and truth, we receive wonderful opportunities to arrive in the present moment and experience a deeply authentic connection. By listening to what's being said and ignoring our agenda of time and schedules, we are taught the most important lesson from an authentic source.

Time is presented in a linear fashion. A timeline draws back from the past and onwards to a future that has not yet become. In the intermediate zone somewhere in the middle is now – yet we can't fully settle here. But this is the awakening zone. It is the mountain ridge of the present moment. It is our oneness with breath. There is nowhere else to awaken, there is nothing else to do and there is no place else to go. *Now* is a mental portal, or better still, a non-mental portal, of awakening which we are moving further and further away from in our busy culture.

I remember when information technology first came into the workplace. I was a student, and the great hope was that this would lead to a reduction in workload and an enrichment in the quality of life for all. Despite the exponential surface benefits and changes it has brought to our lives, we are working harder and are more switched on than ever. There is a whole generation who are addicted to screens, and switching off is not even an option. Screens magnify the opportunities for distraction and hurry and amplify the noise, making it appear that we are always busy, always on. But we are not on; we are off. The present moment has never been so buried under the hurry, busyness, and distraction as it is now. And it is all going to get even more hectic in the future. It doesn't have to be. Every new development is neutral; it is what we do with it and how we perceive it that adds the spin. Paradoxically, what had the potential to increase contact and connectivity is now creating isolation and mental health issues. We are more and more isolated in our individual silos than ever before. Stopping to take micro-moments of *now* within our day is increasingly essential for our sanity and mental health.

When we meet someone who is not in a hurry, it is truly one of the most reassuring and uplifting experiences, yet it is so rare. The feeling they send out to us is one of presence and calm. They are fully available now, and not rushing to get out of it. They choose in this moment not to subscribe to Gen H. They are communicating: 'I am here'. When we say someone seems to have time, we find ourselves marvelling in envy. We want this! These unhurried people we meet, like the fun-loving students, are inviting us to be here now and not to rush out of it.

◌ Let's breathe

Breathing space	The No-Hurry Breath
Duration	Four Conscious Breaths
Response	To be here now
Best for	Regular repeated practice
Outcome	To slow it all down

Plant your feet on the floor. This tells your mind you are grounded and going nowhere for a bit.

Now take a conscious breath. Were you in a hurry just then? When we observe ourselves in a hurry, we wake up to what we have lost. What was the hurry about? Where were you rushing to? A conscious breath brings direct awareness to the here and now.

Once we have remembered what we have lost, we are halfway there. Now, with your feet still planted, take three more conscious breaths to deepen your awareness of being here now.

Breathe and be here now.

Breathe.

Chapter 4

Who's in the Driver's Seat?

In his book *The Chimp Paradox*, the author, Professor Steve Peters, helps us to understand the interactions between the emotional and rational parts of our brain.[3]

He calls the impulse side of our brain the chimp. Everyone has an inner chimp; it's the limbic system and the centre of our emotions. The good news is we have an inner human too. It's located in our prefrontal cortex. The chimp survived and thrived in the world of 'no' when life was so much more dangerous. It was designed to make snap decisions and was obsessed with primal needs of food, sex and immediate danger. Our chimp kept us safe. It made us fight when we needed to fight, run when we needed to run, kill when we needed to kill. It was our hero. It was jealous and greedy – and it still is. It demanded our attention – and it still does…

But more than attention, more than anything, our chimp seeks re-assurance. It is happiest when it knows that our inner human is driving the bus. Then it can sit back and relax, no longer needing to be on the lookout. The key to this reassurance for our chimp is *relaxed attention.* Take note here as we will return to these two words.

When a coin is tossed, it comes up heads or tails. A referee tosses a coin to see who kicks off. If it's heads, one team chooses and the other doesn't, and if it's tails, the options are flipped. It's a binary 'you win – I lose: you lose – I win' approach to choice. 'Yes' and 'no' are opposite sides of the same coin. A 'yes' to this means a 'no' to that, and vice versa. We frequently make these decisions. Sometimes we don't know we've made them and are unaware that a decision has been taken or are unconscious of the process. Every time we do one thing, we are not doing another. Even doing nothing is a choice over doing something.

Thousands of years ago we lived in a world of 'no'. We were hardwired for a few basic decisions – will I eat it, will it eat me, can I mate with it, can I outrun it? In a dangerous, unknown environment, 'no' kept us safe. Paradoxically, breakthroughs happened when we said 'yes' in this world – 'yes' to a new food, 'yes' to fire, 'yes' to another group. 'Yes' was countercultural and it was the growth path.

Now the coin has flipped. We are living in a world of constant opportunity which is designed for us to say 'yes'. Except it's a lazy yes because we are often unconscious at worst or not fully awake at best when making it. It's a world of impulse rather than one of reflection and taking stock.

When we emerge from being online, we often have no idea where and how long we have been there or what we have been doing, which is exactly the intention. We can emerge with a pervasive unremembering, a kind of brain fog indicating we have been unconscious for so much of the time. It's like we have been in a parallel world designed to make us this way and amenable to suggestion – we have. Big tech companies such as Amazon and Netflix know this ground well and so guide us down what are known as rabbit-hole algorithms.

When information reaches the brain, it reaches our chimp first, and when we react, a decision has been taken out of our hands because our chimp is rooted in reaction and never response. Our chimp brain trumped our human brain back then and it trumps our human brain now – if we let it. Look again at the quote by Rollo May at the start of the book – and know that we can change our outcomes by calming our chimp down with just one conscious breath.

Whilst on the surface there is much less danger around, the modern world is golden for our chimps. Canvassing is for chimps, tabloid headlines are for chimps, and so is Instagram. Our modern world is being designed to dumb us down and numb us down into a conditioned 'yes'. We are being bombarded to become unconscious. Whereas in the past the growth path was to say 'yes' in a dangerous world, today the growth path is to say 'no' in a world of unlimited opportunity which has been socially engineered to make us unconscious. The growth path is non-reaction and takes time. Time to wake up and settle our chimp down and to make reasoned, reflected responses with our human brain and not our reactive chimp. It's time to consciously breathe.

How are you breathing now?

Consider road rage: it happens when our chimp gets behind the wheel and meets another chimp en route. We may be travelling in our modern cars on highly engineered roads, but the evolutionary clock can just click back thousands of years. Recently I took a long journey in a traffic jam on a motorway south of London to Birmingham in a thunderstorm. I was driving with my mother in her very old car to a relative's funeral 200 miles away. We were looking forward to the journey as an opportunity to catch up, and my mother was deep in conversation, oblivious to the external conditions. My chimp should have had a field day. Except it didn't. It knew that I was relaxed and at the wheel and so it relaxed. I was breathing consciously using an internal technique I had learned that gave auditory feedback to the brain. It is called ujjayi breathing. My tongue was placed in the roof of my mouth so I could control my breath more and get internal auditory feedback – silent for the passenger but audible to me and my chimp. I was in a relaxed yet alert state ideally suited to navigating complexity. Generally, when we are relaxed, we are asleep or unconscious, and often when we are alert, our chimp is at the wheel, ready to pounce. Our *relaxed alertness* highlighted earlier is the holy grail and a theme that I will return to.

I have a friend who introduced me to his chimp whom he names Fionn after an Irish warrior figure. He actively talks to it to calm it down and reassure it. I am forever grateful for this lesson. Words can get me back in thought and would be something for my ego to jump on, and my chimp would jump at the noise. For me, calming my chimp is best done with conscious breathing. In calming the chimp, we open the possibility for life to lead us.

Realising there are two sides to the coin, we get to make choices with our chimp relaxed. Here we understand the yes in a 'yes' and the yes in a 'no' – and we get to make fully conscious decisions with our human brain and not our chimp.

Diversity, creativity and authenticity come from making conscious choices whereas socially conditioned outcomes come from socially conditioned inputs. Paradoxically, in this time of so much surface abundance and choice, never have there been so many programmes and traps out there intended to keep us unconscious. In this way, our chimp is still right about it being unsafe out there, but it doesn't have the sophistication to help us navigate the complexity of the modern world. We need to take responsibility for how we interact with our world. When we walk our intensely busy modern paths as pilgrims of relaxed alertness, we become more authentic and calm our inner chimp.

Our emotional state is reflected in our breath. It is good to see how we are breathing to know how we are feeling. The emotional coin can then be flipped by taking just one conscious breath. Breathing it we are back in the driving seat.

◯ Let's breathe

Breathing reflection

How are you breathing now? Check in with yourself. Take a moment to notice where your breath sits – shoulders, belly, chest? Relaxed alertness flows from conscious breathing. When doing something, take a breath and ask, 'What am I doing now? Am I awake or am I asleep?' Try to see if you have gone unconscious – have you been led down a rabbit hole online? Conscious breathing enables you to discern this yes in 'no' and the yes in 'yes'.

Breathe.

Chapter 5

The Unbundling
of No-Thing

When last did you or your children play pass the parcel?

The spiritual journey we undertake is rather like the children's game of pass the parcel played at birthday parties. In preparation for this, the party hosts will wrap a small present in birthday paper. The present is then covered in newspaper and secured tightly with tape. This action is repeated, again and again, taping the parcel down tighter with every turn so the contents remain hidden and not available too soon. As the wrapping continues, the parcel balloons in size, with the gift concealed deep within its core.

There is one layer for each child, and always a couple more just in case. Then the package is finished off with a decorative flourish of paper, sometimes boxes, ribbon, and tape. This small gift becomes a thing of wonder and anticipation, often put on display for all the children to see when they arrive at the party.

The moment arrives. All the children sit on the floor in a circle. Music starts and the puffy, weighted parcel is passed around and around. The trick for each child is in grasping the parcel for as long as the music keeps playing and peer group pressure permits, before releasing it with a flourish to speed up the process of return. When the music stops, in the silence of the pause, whoever has the package gets to unwrap a layer. Naturally, each child tears into it as quickly as possible until the music resumes and the parcel is passed around again. Off it goes until every child has participated and the end is in sight. Finally, the birthday paper is revealed. The gift is back where it started – but the game, the anticipation, and the fun and lengthy process of unbundling has added so much more.

Our journey of awakening is like this. On the outer leg we bundle up and bundle up, becoming someone in the eyes of the world. As we do so we become a little tighter and bigger, more impressive perhaps, but generally further from our core in the process. Our final outer layer of fine clothes, often reflecting our social status, is rather like the ribbon on the parcel, a statement of value and comparison. Once we can stand back from ourselves and see this reflection, we start the process of awakening and turn for home.

On the return home, everything is reversed; in the silence of our awareness, we shed many layers of our skin. This is the simplicity of letting go. With each transition we stop, pause and prepare to shed another layer, unbundling a little more and a little more each time. In the depths of experience and awareness, our heart softens, just as the centre of the parcel gets squishy and misshapen by the many hands tearing at the tape and the paper. We become more human, smaller with each passage of unbundling, and closer and closer to the heart of who we are. When we get to the final layer, our being – which is our deepest wrapper – is revealed.

It is here we are a fraction of who we were. Our egoic shell of our worldly identity diminishing and in the shedding of all the outer layers.

My own big unbundling had its own era: Covid. The pandemic hit me hard, and late, but now I know it had to be exactly like this. Just as I thought I had escaped it and gone through a traumatic phase at work, it struck me and I was told I had to rest – which was not my mind's best friend.

The idea of doing nothing was a pain. I was reared to wake up, get on and get out. But this time I had no choice. Doing nothing was the only available option. And I loathed it. At the time, I was coming to the end of my breathing sessions on the river barge. I felt a need to contact my breath worker for a chat – maybe some sympathy too. I got the opposite. She told me to shut up, wise up and rest up. Tough love but just what I needed to hear. I had to embrace what I have for so long needed. It was like a well-timed smack of awakening that Zen masters specialise in. *Whack.*

I just had to let go, and acquire another foreign concept that I clearly had not mastered – *surrender*. Always working and preoccupied, even through years of meditation, surrender was not something I had a hold on – apparently, that was the point. Not to have a hold on it but just to let it. Despite my decided new journey of conscious living, well into my fifties, I somehow would always default to busyness. The more I did, the more I felt useful, and in control. It's a good feeling, but it should not be a permanent one.

Being sick and allowing myself to be sick, I finally got real respite from my deepest malaise – an almost genetic inability to let go and surrender. But this time the wisdom of the body was talking, and my ego which had carried the torch for all this intergenerational resistance had to finally listen and obey. I could not battle my way through. I had to stop and rest and let the body do what it needed to. To take control of the wheel. Once I allowed it, everything changed, literally everything. Finally, belatedly and begrudgingly, my ego surrendered, and I let go into the sickness. The other side of it I got better and finally knew the importance of surrendering to the flow of life. Then everything went and changed all over again.

On my return to work, I was smaller, a little less at the centre of things, not in a bad way, possibly in a quieter way of the heart. I took more of a back seat and watched as the energy of things guided me and our community. Sometimes I would act, but only when called upon. My more-surrendered self knew I didn't need to be the leader or the fixer all the time. There was no need, as I had a deeper trust in the play of life. I recall this as a blessed time in my life. My becoming smaller enabled others to grow and feel supported – which was an unexpected gift.

The passage of bundling up and unbundling through life is a bit like the clothes we put on and shed as we climb and descend a mountain. If we also focus on our breath as we go, we see that during the ascent we inhale more deeply to get air into our lungs, while on the way down we are more mindful and exhale with breaths of letting go and greater ease. Later, this idea will be developed into the concept of one breath of becoming and surrender, known as the *cosmic breath*.

○ Let's breathe

Breathing space	The Awakened Breath
Duration	60 seconds
Response	To centre my thoughts and awaken my senses
Best for	Points of transition; low energy end of the workday
Outcome	Revived spirit; reconnecting with who I am

Take a breath. Imagine you are the parcel being passed around the room. With your inhale, envisage yourself as the tightly bundled 'I am'. See layer after layer of the day's accumulation. Hold the inhale for two beats. Now exhale, and let go of it all. Repeat three times. Regular practice throughout the day of this conscious breath will deliver best results.

Breathe.

Chapter 6
Awakening From Stuff

On the outward journey of life, we bundle up and all our stuff accumulates over time.

This becomes personal dust that we seek to uncover later in life. The process of waking up to all this stuff and to our true self corresponds to the final lap of the outer journey of life. At this point our stuff and mess becomes our message. We need to see our stuff to break free of it.

So let's talk about clutter. Physical clutter is easy – we can see it clearly and trip over it. This clutter is a bit like the stalactites and stalagmites accumulated and formed over time in the cave of our life. While this is physical, mental clutter is subtler and often goes undetected. We only see it when we open up a gap and take a perceptual step out of it. This mental clutter trips us up too. The process of mental decluttering is initiated when we take the first step outside of mind identification.

Breathwork was the most powerful method of doing this for me. I came to understand that without clarity of purpose and clear intention, the aisles of my mind rather like over-stacked supermarket shelves become a source of overwhelm and one big head-trip hazard. With one conscious breath, we start to understand and change this. The nature of the mind is to desire, desire, desire, and everything on the shelves looks so tempting. But with time and understanding, we see this and introduce some wisdom into the situation. Seeing this is the start of freeing us from our stuff.

With the breath we introduce space to a situation and a gap opens between the stimulus and what happens next. In choosing how we respond to a situation, we start on the path of self-determination and freedom. From here we can go on to respond to events rather than react to them. I think about this as our *wisdom gap*. Our wisdom gap is responsive and non-reactive, and there is no room for our chimp inside. Rather like the state of relaxed attention highlighted earlier, this is where you want to be.

To help us reach the wisdom gap, we need to understand 'stuff'. All kinds of stuff. The stuff that triggers us, the stuff that weighs us down, the stuff we trip over, the stuff we can't see. Just stuff. I've taken the liberty to rummage through the Stuff Attic here – bring a lamp!

The stuff of life: clutter

Sandstone is formed when sand and sediment is compacted over thousands of years into a block of stone. We think of them as rocks but really, they are just very compressed blocks of sand. And once they are rocks, returning to the softness of sand is highly unlikely, or at least will take a good many of our lifetimes to get there. Look out for those rocks as we come back to them later.

In the very same way, our stuff accumulates and hardens. It doesn't take thousands of years but over our lifetime, we start to identify with the rock rather than the sand, and the space that enables it. As the emotional clutter and eons of our personal stuff harden, we become less flexible, more cynical, less adaptable, and we build our layers further and further from our true selves. The sediments that form the stone of our identity are the accumulated thoughts and emotions that we give to situations that we think of as our history and our life. These things that we start to identify with are really the spin and reaction we give to otherwise neutral events. They become set in stone. This becomes our self-identity but it is really our false self-identity. This is because our truest and deepest identity lies in the space within and surrounding these things and events, rather than our mind-based interpretation and identification in response to them.

When consciously breathing, we catch glimpses of this process. What we see is that we are not our mind but rather, we are the space we are observing it with. We are the observer rather than the observed. Not the easiest thing to get your head around, I know. But this concept is not to be overthought – rather felt.

In my breathwork sessions, I have experienced the sensation of 'being breathed'. Picture that. A sense that I was no longer breathing but, instead, being breathed by the spirit of my breath. I began to experience my source and intuitively sensed its source – the breath within my breath. I experienced that this is who I am rather than the person breathing. At its deepest level, the 'I' that I was, was the source of the breath rather than the 'I' that identified with the person doing the breathing. This is the portal of consciousness that we can enter once we start to breathe away some of our clutter.

Many of us have experienced the catharsis and spaciousness that follow a physical declutter. It's the same with our mental clutter. Seeing is freeing, so when we can see our mental clutter, we start the process of freeing ourselves of it. We become lighter and freer in this process. We see things as they are without any mind-made interpretation; we get in touch with the being of ourselves and everything around us – the source of which is the breath within the breath.

Conscious breathing is a powerful way to start to see and eventually free us of the mental clutter and blow away the dust of our lives. By taking time to reflect on the contents of our mind – what we are and what we have become – we can start the process of decluttering, or 'brain pruning' as it is referred to by neuroscientists. For most people, this awakening to our truth does not happen overnight. It takes a while to unbundle the package of our life.

With mental decluttering, we see the rock we wish to break down. We choose in this moment to chip away at the historical stones and emotional clutter built up over eons, and we start to be free, here and now.

◯ Let's breathe

Breathing space	The Wisdom Gap Breath
Duration	60 seconds
Response	To become the observer of your mind
Best for	Seeing things clearly; detaching from your thoughts
Outcome	A happier, more responsive and less reactive you

Take a breath and become the observer. See yourself watching the chitter-chatter of your mind. Observe it, like a spider watching a web it has just created. If you see something catch in the web, let it be. Watch it neutrally and label it 'thought'. It's just a thought. Don't poke it;

don't feed it by exploring it and following up with more thoughts. Just sit. Watch. Wait and watch. By doing this, notice how your stuff blows away naturally, and thoughts die of their own accord.

Breathe.

More stuff because of other stuff

In the West, we are born into a world where we are hardwired to consume; an acquisitive mindset that tells us more is more. More stuff means more status and more happiness. Our economies are set up that way and their performance is measured by the additional stuff we produce each year. The focus for economies that do not consume their own stuff is to sell it abroad. Ship it (or even worse, air freight it) halfway across the world. We are like magpies and our stuff takes on a life of its own, creating the need for more stuff.

Just as we are conditioned into thinking we need all this material stuff, it's far worse and subtler with our thoughts, and our mental stuff. When we identify with our thoughts, we think we are the contents of our mind, but in fact we are putting our attention in the wrong place. Worse still, when we identify with the endless thoughts in our head, we are unsatisfiable.

This identification with the thoughts in our head is rather like normalising and unconsciously accepting a neighbour's burglar alarm continuously going off. You know the kind. The deafening sound that goes on for far too long, it becomes the 'normal' sound. Your ear picks it up as white noise, not disturbance. That is, until the alarm stops. It is in the sheer relief of silence that we can finally comprehend the depth of intrusion. We understand that the pervasive ringing in our ears left us with no headspace – our minds were completely hijacked by that alarm. Eknath Easwaran, who wrote a verse-by-verse commentary on the Bhagavad Gita, says that we don't really have a thought as such; it has us – and it goes on and on unchecked, the clutter of thoughts ever spiralling in all directions.

Like stuff creates stuff, mental clutter begets mental clutter. In the middle, our minds are beep-bopping, not giving us a moment of peace. When these spiralling thoughts carry an emotional charge, they become so much more powerful. They start to attract and vacuum up like-minded thoughts and like-minded people by association. Notice the rock – giving us the illusion of permanence. We have become conditioned for this, sometimes even educated for it, by the pursuit of more thoughts, more facts, more knowledge.

What we identify with is our 'own spin' – the eons of accumulated emotional charges which we put on otherwise neutral thoughts and events.

In some mental health issues, the negative self-talk can be so all-consuming and powerful that anything will be done to dial it down. Certain eating disorders, particularly among young girls, have been linked to emotional regulation.[4] It is possible that these distract the mind because when the body is starving, all that it can communicate is its primal need for food. This need becomes a constant obsession which is preferable to the negative emotional state that it masks. Among many strategies, conscious breathing can help here, as it can stop identification with our mental state. In this way conscious breathing can be a path to freedom from identification with the thoughts in our mind.

The first step on this path to freedom is to see that these identities of the mind are not us at our deepest core, and so they do not define us. They survive and thrive because we put our attention in the wrong place. Let's breathe it in.

Social stuff

Until the summer of 2023, I worked in a small school for children with autism and complex needs, which provided lots of opportunities for reflection and learning. One of the children I worked with loved the song 'The Wheels on the Bus' and would happily improvise on versions of it on a loop when at play in the garden. Rather like the wheels of our mind, the wheels on the bus just keep on turning.

As I was singing along with him one day, I thought of another version for my own benefit:

The wheels of the mind, go jibber-jabber jibber-jabber,
jibber-jabber jibber-jabber, jibber-jabber jibber-jabber;
The wheels of the mind go jibber-jabber jibber-jabber, all
day long.

Today, with almost universal access to handheld devices there has been an exponential explosion in jibber-jabber and a corresponding reduction in peace. It is no surprise that anxiety is going round and round and is now part of the vocabulary of the incredibly young. This constant stream of information and opinions does not help us switch off – nor does it make us happier or even more knowledgeable – we have become a scroll-for-more society – yet more stuff! We're exposed to endless trivia, endlessly distracted, endlessly on, and endlessly on edge.

It feels that we have reached a tipping point. We have become so overwhelmed with mental clutter that it has encroached on our well-being and on our ability to discern what is of value. The jibber-jabber of our thoughts is being exponentially multiplied online and it's of no value. Worse, it's making us sick. We are crying out for peace. Even the founder of Meta (Facebook) has publicly admitted that they made it as addictive as possible and that they are now worried about the mental health of their young users.[5] More information has led to less wisdom.

Real knowing or wisdom breaks free of the ever-spinning wheels of identification with jibber-jabber and comes from a different place altogether. It comes from a place of stillness. Our own quiet still aliveness is the source of who we are. We can only access it when we are still and free of thoughts.

In a recent talk, Eckhart Tolle says his greatest achievement is to stop thinking at will, likened to a state of Zen.[6] No huge claims. Just that. The ability to turn off the thought stream. Another spiritual teacher, this time of the last century, was Krishnamurti. In his biography it states that from an early age, he was groomed to be an enlightened being and teacher called the 'World Teacher' by The Theosophical Society in India.[7] He had tens of thousands of people following him as a very young man. In later life he would often start a talk by saying that if you understood what he was saying, you should leave. Krishnamurti saw truth as a pathless path and that a life of attracting followers despite himself was not the way; he had to leave and physically get off stage for people to find their truth. He dissolved all the institutions set up to follow him and stopped giving public talks. Later in life, he fully returned to himself by simply walking in the woods, when not a single thought would come to mind.

We start to see that when we begin to experience ourselves in this space of no thought, there is something beyond that space. Wisdom and inspiration flow when we turn off our identification with our thought stream. Advanced meditators often think of a thought as a train pulling into the station: we can observe it, know where it has come from, and decide if we are going to hop on or not. Contrast that with the infinitely converging and diverging tracks of thought we all seem to be compulsively hurtling down. Awareness is key and our authentic self has the conditions to flow when we understand that we are not our thoughts.

Education needs to reflect the need for more space, less scroll. With knowledge and facts the swipe of a screen away, what we need from students is not what they have learned from YouTube or TikTok but rather something different: we need them to tap into their creativity and authenticity. We need them to find their wisdom gap – which does not come from Instagram. As breathers, readers, parents and leaders we must help students bypass the endless tracks of their minds and the false self-identification that is based on them. Thich Nhat Hanh told the story of the student, the glass of water and the monk.[8] The monk offered the student a glass of water, which became cloudy and disturbed in the pouring. Sediment was stirred up in the movement of the water. The student declined the glass as it was dirty and not suitable for drinking. The monk told the student to go off and return in a while. On her return the glass was clear, and the sediment had fallen to the bottom of the glass. The monk explained that the glass was like the mind that needs to be still; then, and only then, can we experience the clarity which is our true state. The pupil drank from the glass.

◯ Let's breathe

Breathing space	For the Wisdom Breath
Duration	15 seconds and five thoughts
Response	To centre my thoughts and awaken my senses
Suited to	All workers
Best for	Initiating tough conversations; end of the workday; low energy
Outcome	Revived spirit; reconnecting with 'I am'

Take a full conscious breath now. Feel a slow inhale through the nose and a low and slow exhale through the mouth. Wait in the glorious spaciousness that follows. Try and experience and feel it. Now watch your mind like the spider watches its web. When a thought comes in, label it 'thought'. Wait until you have counted five thoughts. Then take another conscious breath to finish. Enjoy this space and repeat as often as you can through the day.

Breathe.

Chapter 7

Ego. Put it in Your Pocket.

The ego. Many of us shudder at the word.

Pretty much all of us, in one way or another, are run by it. It is like the mental hamster wheel we endlessly run around. Our job is to know it and set ourselves free. But what is it? As we progress with our training of the mind and our unlearning of old patterns, it is important that we meet our ego first. We can't eliminate it because it is part of us, but we can know it and we can befriend it. Then, with practice and awareness, when it pops up, we can see it and start to respond differently. In first seeking to understand it, we prepare the ground to coexist in a friendly way.

Earlier it was said that our inner spaciousness and mental stillness are who we most fundamentally are. This is like the rest in being after we take one conscious breath. Here we are at one with the energetic centre of everything. This is our being. All the mental distractions and images which prevent us from seeing this or block our access to it are aspects of ego.

There are two forms of identification with ego. The *first aspect* comes when we recognise ourselves as being the outer packaging of the worldly bundle of 'I am'.

Let's explore this, by unpacking what mine is. This is the identity I built up, primarily in the first half of my life, from identification with my past and how people reacted to that. It's like looking through a photo album of my life and seeing a collage of who I became.

As we grow and develop in the world, we bundle ourselves up from our birth. But in doing so we become distanced from a deeper awareness of who we are. As an example, let's explore who I have bundled up to become in the world. I am a:

- partner,
- friend,
- father,
- brother,
- son,
- Englishman by birth,
- Irish resident by choice,
- conscious breather,
- community member,
- gardener,
- pilgrim,
- Leeds United supporter,
- listener (especially to music),
- drinker (and abstainer) of hoppy beer in wonderful company,
- traveller,
- tree lover, and
- sometimes obsessive.

Make your own 'I am' list now. Keep it handy; you will need it at the end of this section.

Our form has now been described in the world of form. But this is not us. This is not the true source of 'I am'. This is identification with our photos, labels, roles, functions, and consequences of the past. It is our history, how we appear to the outside world, and how we can initially appear to ourselves. So many feelings and identities are bundled up in these statements with the possibility of thousands, if not millions, of corresponding thoughts and images. They are not who we are, so do not identify with them. When we identify, we become the worldly bundled 'I am' with all feelings and thoughts thoroughly packaged up in it.

Our real 'I am' is knowing of the silence and spaciousness at the heart of who we really are. The moment we add the word 'a' and we become 'I am a...', we add clutter. Now, instead of the unwrapping and unbundling of the parcel in the introduction, let's try something different; let's prune back. Take out your imaginary pruning shears. You are a beautiful rose that has flowered and needs a period of rest and dormancy before flowering again. Gardeners know that roses need to be pruned back hard. Prune the stems back – cut out the 'I am this' and 'I am that'. Keep pruning until all the 'I am' stems have gone. By pruning back hard you return to the rootstock; you prune back to your core. You have now become 'I am' by a process of reduction of 'who I am not'.

This process of not aligning ourselves with 'I am' nor defining ourselves by it gives us space. When we enter this space, we see that everything is contained in it. We enter a kind of unity through knowing this *no-thing*.

We do not all have to take out the pruning shears to get to our rootstock. Some people get there directly by surrendering to their suffering. As an example, recently I had the opportunity to listen to someone talk of their dependence on drugs and alcohol which took hold so deeply and at such a young age that they were left with nothing.[9] He woke up in a cell with a forensic scientist. He was unsure of who he was and unable to say how he got there. Then having cleaned up and gotten sober in later life, he was ready to move on to a more sustainable place. He was ready for the next phase and was preparing his CV for job applications. He wrote his name. Then everything else was uncertain. He had been experiencing drug dependence for a period, left school at thirteen, and was alone. He didn't need to prune back as in the recognition of the pit of his suffering, he was already there. Having worked with this and having started meditating in jail, he fully surrendered everything and experienced freedom.

The *second aspect* with ego is when we think we are our feelings or emotions. At our deepest core we are not our rage, anger, envy, worry, anxiety. These are temporary expressions of what we identify with. They are so strong and pervasive that we think what is going on in our head now is who we are. But personal identification with these emotions is a distraction from source. In a way they are the ego creating momentum for itself, keeping us spinning around. This theme is spiralled back to later, particularly when we examine fear.

In this book you will read the phrase 'what we resist persists' quite frequently. It applies to so many areas of our life; when we resist, it's like we are trying to block the flow of a river, and it is never truer than when writing about ego. Here's the story. We have ego. A bit like our chimp, it has a job to help us navigate the world as we mature and to keep us safe. It won't go away. Know it, accept it, befriend it, keep it in your pocket. That way you are not reinforcing it with negative energy. Resisting ego is as pointless as the earlier example of not thinking about pink camels.

We suffer for the 'I am' that we are not. This is ego at its biggest play. Suffering, however, when it comes our way, is a great teacher; it is the stimulus that gets so many of us looking for truth. Life, like many of the neurodivergent children I have come to know, keeps knocking at our door until we let go of what is not truly authentic and let our true selves in. Through suffering we finally return to our rootstock.

So whether the 'I am' is a temporary identification with the feeling we are feeling, or a more fixed view of what we have become in this world, we are distracted and taken away from our being. We are taken away from our 'I am', our source. Later I will write about the cosmic breath. We are all on our way there. It is a breath that comes with consciousness, enlightenment and knowing the centrality of love. But none of us are ready until we are ready. This readiness begins by knowing our ego and befriending it. When you have, attach it to your key ring and place it in your pocket.

With our key ring safely in our pocket, the next phase is to jump from the precipice, or let go of everything we know and understand. We return to this later.

○ Let's breathe

> **Breathing reflection**
>
> In our essence, our universal 'I am' is the centre of no-thing at the heart of the parcel and, in a way, everything added after that 'I am' is life clutter.
>
> Give yourself time now to reflect on your list of bundled 'I am' identities. These are not you but rather different expressions that distract you from your deeper identity. Can you prune them back?

How are you breathing now?

Similarly, can you identify with the strong core emotional states that seem to take you over and distract you from source? Remember that while they are strong, they are not who you really are. They obscure you from your inner truth and inner guidance.

How are you breathing now?

Breathe.

Chapter 8

Active Stillness
Within the Trigger

The settled glass reflects the clear mind, yet this mind is far from inactive; inner stillness is fundamentally alive.

Consider all the momentous things that are undramatically choreographed in a quiet dance without any human thought or input whatsoever. They all dance despite us rather than because of us. As we cannot interfere, there is no option but to let it all be. Yet we are our own cosmos – think of the quiet continuous dance that happens in our body soundlessly and without any conscious thought on our part. There is universal energy guiding everything, and it is there for us to tap into. We have been given these amazing bodies to appreciate what is inside of us so that we can appreciate what is beyond. In this way, going within everything is revealed.

The first step of the process of going within is to understand what is not real – this is the ego which is created by the thinking mind. And the thinking mind is the shotgun mind. The moment our thinking mind gets in the way, it starts to feel it is in control and begins to meddle, and a natural equilibrium is disturbed. The sources of the acting out of our impulses are sometimes called our triggers and these are explored below.

Working with children with autism provides an opportunity for self-reflection. Their authenticity demands our own as they are reflecting a mirror of truth back at us. What they primarily want from us are two things: our authenticity, and the clarity with which we express it. Complicated projections do not wash. One day our school was offered a piano out of the blue. I went along with a colleague to have a look and listen to it. The sound was lovely and the light ash that it was made from would look great in the entrance hall of the old convent that was now our school. But we had no staff members who felt they could play it to a sufficient level. I contacted the local music conservatory and one student offered to play for us. I said that we were not an easy gig; our students could be a hard crowd and some of their behaviours could be a trigger for one another. He was undaunted and told us a little about his story and his own journey of authenticity and truth. As a pianist it was clear that he listened deeply within and played from there. He played as if the silence in the music was the source of the notes. Playing in this way the music had an inner voice. This felt intuitively different and more spacious than playing from a more outer voice where the notes were understood to be the source of the music. The key to his playing was his inner stillness and sensitivity of his listening, which became a guiding spaciousness in his playing. The playing was deeply authentic and very clearly communicated and felt part-music, part-meditation. The children picked up on this instinctively and he was able to keep a large group of them together and listening in a way that would not have been possible if he hadn't been playing from a quiet and clear authenticity.

Helping neurodivergent children to understand themselves allows them to regulate their emotions. It takes careful observation to try to establish the trigger that can set off a complex pattern of behaviour. There will always be something and it may be what we least expect. Once we have the trigger, it's rather like cracking a code because we are on the way to explaining the source of a behavioural reaction to the child and us. Some neurodivergent children are so sensitive to essence and mood that anything other than positive attention is a trigger. With these children, just being in a positive space and framing things attentively enables them to avoid reacting negatively to bad news or disappointments. Tone and space rather than content are key.

As an example, horse riding was a favourite activity among the children at school, and some would ask for it daily, for weeks and months in advance. One week it had to be cancelled at very short notice. For some children this was devastating news and a potentially significant trigger across the school. It was handled for one child with such sensitivity and awareness by a colleague that the news was completely accepted without incident. Breaking bad news with compassion is a rare gift. Stepping back to understand the significance of the news is half the journey – the rest is giving space so what we say is touched with our inner wisdom and compassion.

For those of us who are not neurodivergent, our behaviours are subtler, sometimes less honest and direct, and our triggers can be more disguised and buried. But as we start to awaken to our overidentification with the pervasive thoughts in our head, we understand ourselves more and can start to see the trails, like wisps of cloud, that may have triggered us. With self-awareness, we start to understand and explore the triggers that lead to self-destructive behaviour and thought patterns. Irrespective of the trigger and the behaviour that follows, the result is always the same – when we react to a trigger, we are set off and are drawn away from our authenticity.

Working with our triggers can help set us free. There is a very successful programme which changes behaviour around alcohol consumption. Our triggers (or cravings) to drink or whatever we crave are interpreted as wake-up calls, which are opportunities for awareness and gratitude that we are actively changing. Each trigger refocuses desire and craving and enables us to express our gratitude for the conscious and new choices we are making. Let's explore my backstory with alcohol here.

Consistent drinking played a part in our family growing up. I remember Sunday lunchtimes with my dad and grandad. They would be inside the pub drinking a couple of lunchtime pints; I was ten or so and would be outside, sitting on a ledge, drinking ginger beer and eating crisps served through a hatch in the side door by dad. Children weren't allowed in pubs in those days. In this way, the pub and its beer pumps became the forbidden pleasure that I was destined to drink deeply from in later life.

My grandfather was a beer drinker; whisky when he got the price of a bottle. Dad graduated to become a red wine drinker. For Dad and his friends, red wine was the generational holy grail, a great way to spend rising disposable income, a lovely mellowness with no known downside.

Dad had to contend with a lot. He had done well from a tough start. Keeping on top of things was more difficult than he would sometimes dare to let on. A glass or two of red after work helped. It masked everything but, in becoming an outlet, it possibly buried deeper truths. Fortunately, both Dad and I had an off button so never tipped over the edge. We were both middle-lane drinkers – not too fast, not too slow – but getting there in our own time.

Possibly my biggest problem with drink was that I did not look at it for so long. I grew into it young. I made my own beer at fourteen – my way of getting in the side door underage. At fifteen, I was illicitly supplying neighbours and became quite good. This led to a Saturday job in a homebrew shop. At college, a lot of my grant was spent in the junior common room and the local pub. As I started work, weekends in the pub and with friends became a refuge from the straitjacket of office life. And on and on and on it went. Never tipping over the edge, just going too far, too fast, for too long. Middle-lane drinking with middle-lane cravings.

One could say that my 'I am' was a drinker, in denial. Uncorking all this and examining it has taken forty years – way too long. I have stopped for a good bit. Yes, I sometimes miss it. I miss the bitterness of hops, the mellowness of a glass of red wine, and the sweetness of a glass of old whisky. At first I also missed the times when I was bored or overwhelmed and just wanted to dial things down a notch. But this is a small price to pay; my anxiety has gone – I was drinking alcohol to mask something that it created.

The key in overcoming our triggers is to get our thoughts out of the way and align with the natural energy that quietly runs through our body. Then we can remove the gun from our head, stop obsessing with our cravings, and let it all be. Getting ourselves out of the way is the process of disidentification with the ego, and then allowing what is left to flow.

◯ Let's breathe

Breathing space	The Stillness Breath
Duration	10 seconds
Response	To centre my thoughts and explore my motivations
Best for	Strain and weakened will; struggling with cravings
Outcome	Empowerment; reconnecting with your goals

Take a moment now to recall a trigger today. With one fully conscious breath, breathe it in, hold the feeling it conveys for two beats, notice any body tightness – and slowly, exhale a long breath for eight counts. Allow the feeling to be, and let it go. Repeat three times. Ask a kindness from your mind: request your unconscious mind to support you the next time you experience a trigger. Ask your mind to remind you to take a conscious breath and interject a gap. You can access the wisest part of yourself this way; by simply asking, the solution that emerges may surprise you.

Breathe.

Chapter 9

The Root of Anger

To tap into our one conscious breath fully, we need to understand a little more about anger, where it comes from, and why.

Righteous anger is a bit like a holy ego: it flatters us in our progress, and gets us entrenched back there. Mine ensnared me for a long time. Looking back, sometimes when I was right, the need to demonstrate it was wrong. Too many waves were created in the pursuit of being right and it was counterproductive at best and destructive at worst. It made me fight against the natural flow, swimming hard upstream, and getting entangled in debris coming my way.

The need to be right came from a strong sense of injustice that I had at an early age. I remember refusing to return to play school as a four-year-old (quite a protest in the traditions of suburban England in the late sixties) because I had been accused of something I hadn't done. My mother was asked to intervene. She was supportive of me once she found the truth and I returned to play school the following day albeit with a neighbour who I felt hadn't sold me out. This all happened without the apology that my older more righteous self would have sought. The roots of this righteous anger go deep, and it would surface whenever people around me were perceived as being unreasonable or dishonest. Like the partisan crowd at the football match, written about later, it was easier and a distraction to point out over there than to sort out the roots of my own stuff.

This later mushroomed into a full holy ego which later grafted onto the career change I had made, and the financial sacrifices involved in moving from a career in business to become a primary school teacher. Letting go means letting go of everything that has been getting in the way. There really is no need to be right, especially if it creates the potential for toxicity. It was clearly holding me back. It's not important who's right or wrong. What's important is being in flow and tapping into the positive energy of that. On the barge I finally learned to let go. That is not to say I let go of everything, forever – there is considerably less anger than I felt a couple of years ago, but I will always need to maintain a practice of conscious breathing to not lose the run of myself.

Can you look back to your childhood to identify the first development of your ego? Was it a spark of anger or injustice that ignited it, as in my case? Can you see how that may still be presenting itself now? What harm is this causing you and others? Is it still serving you or is it holding you back? Can you set an intention to try and let go? These are very valuable themes to bring to a qualified breath worker so you can uncover them and start the process of surrender. With guidance, honesty and the right intention, you can transcend your mind with your breath. You can even identify and transcend ego in the present moment.

Transcending ego, however temporarily, enables us to forgive ourselves for wrong identification with it. We understand that the past has passed. We wake up to the truth that we are all struggling, that we are all flawed. So there is no need to judge. Stop judging yourself and others. Once we become free, we act freely in this way. Although outward forgiveness is for others, the movement of forgiveness is the most powerful thing we can do for ourselves. When we are no longer attached to emotions of past events, they have finally passed and we are free to surrender.

When we let go, we let go of all the impediments on the way – some of these, especially a flattering ego, are there to stop our progress, so we remain captivated by its ways. For me though, even more than a flattering ego, a holy ego is one of the final scenes in the play of the cat and mouse that leads to escape from the ego's depths.

All our false identities and especially our holy false identities must go. We know the big picture when we realise that the ends rarely justify the means. We stop resisting and let things fall away and, in that space, we see the essence of it all and of others.

When people are trusted and given the space to be, they tend to sort things out for themselves. This starts with us in the process of awakening. We don't need our thoughts and ideas so it follows that they don't either. What we all need is shared presence, and love.

Chapter 10

Anger. The Teacher.

'Liberation comes with a change of perception. We need to let things be as they are because life's problems will never end. If we can stay with our awareness, then we will be okay. The only reliable liberation from suffering is not trying to get rid of the problem, then the wave of suffering will not try and get rid of us.'

– Youngey Mingyur Rinpoche

Anger was the big one for me, because it is such a strong energy.

Like removing a fire blanket, once anger is uncovered, the embers of fear and sadness that it smothered can be seen. I am cautious deep down and could only jump free of fear when I knew at a bodily level that I would be safe. I understood that whatever happened, I would breathe and my diaphragmatic parachute would break my fall. Our mind is deeply conservative and a small part of it wants to hang onto what we know. The chimp resists the unknown as they are always on the lookout, keeping us safe. Our dear, unevolved chimp knows well, so well, from its experience, that it is dangerous out there – and there is absolutely no point telling it otherwise! We know that the only thing that reassures our chimp is relaxed attention – and once we have reassured it and calmed that side of ourselves down, we are free of fear and free to let go. For me, this is not a once-and-for-all feeling; rather, it is something I can remember one conscious breath at a time. With each conscious exhale I let go a little bit more. Slowly with each exhale I drift away from fear and open to the possibility of freedom.

When we are captivated by our chimp brain, we can react from a point of anger. A little focused and expressed anger (when we engage our adult brain) can be positive. But too much anger, like an uncontrollable fire, is dangerous and can be toxic for everyone. When we add drugs or alcohol to the mix, it burns dangerously and can quickly get out of control. The worst thing is to hold on. Let's imagine yesterday's play of anger. The drama is over, the actors have walked away, but we are left regurgitating the script and the emotional scenes. This gets into our head. Before we know it, the hamster wheel is off again, creating reality and momentum for itself, affecting our mental health as it spins. It's like we are holding onto a hot stone which is burning us. Drop it. Drop the script, forget the emotions and sack the actors. It has all been and gone. So just let go for your own sake.

The final journey of the route home is to completely let go and, in that letting go, realise that there is always a little more to come. Let go of all your resistance, ambitions, talents, preferences and beliefs. As you let go of these final blockages smile at them on the way because they are probably concealing something of great importance to you. They are like the stones rolled over the cave of your heart. Surrender everything as everything apart from emptiness or no-thing gets in the way. Being free is being free of desire and egoic drive, and it is a very attractive state that enables life to flow through us. Freedom is the universal goal; here we are like the untethered hot air balloon that can be blown on the thermals of life. In this flow, what is for us is for us, and what is not for us is not pursued. By trying not trying, life happens. As we align with our path, we meet people on the way who have the same outlook and energy. They naturally inspire and support us. Like goes to like. Be with people who share your level of consciousness and want to heal. Become a positivity magnet like some of the neurodivergent children I worked with.

We need courage to recognise and surrender to our fear. The more I understood the depth of the courage needed, by association the depth of my fear was known to me. Fear is the seed of all doubts. As a keen gardener, I understood my fear as an invasive species. Much like a poison ivy on a wall that settles in a new place then grows tendrils to secure it before moving onto higher ground. The fear had grown three main stems within me. The fear of lack, the fear of conflict and the fear of disapproval. These have taken root and like an ivy have the capacity to smother its host.

The fear of lack, obscuring what was enough, gave me a mindset of scarcity. I almost became so proficient in delaying gratification that I forgot to be here now. To be mindful of our resources is prudent, but to save in the absence of evidence of its need is also building up reserves from fear. It is a fear that blocks the flow of abundance that we can all tap into when we clear our paths. Hoarding can also take the form of unnecessary stuff and facts which just act as more clutter that conceals the energy of clarity and wisdom within us. It also has us hanging onto previous modalities that are simply not required in a surrendered state. Surrender then is the ultimate internal declutter.

If my misperception of what was enough was a passive side of my fear, then anger was the active one. Anger, which has been written about, is a kind of puffing up of ourselves to safeguard us from attack.

We biologically swell up and say:

'Look at me, I'm really mad. More than that though, I am so righteously mad. So, don't mess with me and my anger!'

But when we lose it, we lose it. To move from this lose-lose we must express anger neutrally with considered words and no action or emotion. Here we have made the conscious shift from reaction to response and have freed ourselves from attachment to anger. When we verbalise anger in a way that doesn't have us swelling up with it, we regain control. A conscious breath before we respond to an event elevates the consciousness of our response. This is our wisdom gap and it invites the opportunity for a win-win response.

For a long time, I thought the expression of anger was a growth path, after the conditioning of earlier life, which was a very loving and supportive home environment overlaid by a kind of calm, socially conditioned homogeneity. In retrospect this was not fully calm; it concealed a kind of unexamined fear. Responding to events with anger felt like progress from this, but it wasn't. Too much emotional anger, as written about earlier, is just as toxic as repressing it. Instead, anger needs to be surrendered and understood. Once we realise that the heat of our anger is the embers of our fear – fear that we are impermanent, wounded and alone – then we have its number. When we express anger neutrally and calmly in words, we douse our embers and source our true power. As the Dalai Lama said, before we work for universal disarmament, we must first go through our own internal disarmament. Peace begins with us from the inside out.[10]

The other manifestation of fear for me was the conditioned desire to be nice, affable, agreeable and to keep everything on the level. To not rock the boat. When we wake up, we wake up to our fullness (paradoxically sometimes referred to as emptiness by some Buddhists) and to everyone else's.[11] Whilst rocking the boat is understandable at the beginning, it has no forward motion, and must be surrendered later on to go with our flow.

I was left with the poison ivy of fear with three stems: lack, anger, and passivity. Seeing is the start of freeing. So, as every gardener knows, removing ivy must be done above ground first. We start by freeing up the adjacent trees and shrubs that have been choking for so long. Then peel the ivy back tendril by tendril, conscious exhale by conscious exhale, so it can be removed. Then, and only then, is the ground clear. But the roots remain. We can cut off the ivy, but with a healthy rootstock, it will reappear and be almost energised by a vigorous prune. To remove it we must dig it up. Get below ground and pull it from the roots. But this stuff is pervasive and persuasive. It wants to cling on physically and mentally, and that's how it has flourished for so long.

The final push is completely counterintuitive; it is to understand there is no final push and that eventually the ivy will let go of its hold on us if we let go of our hold on it. We become free when we realise that our grasping was keeping the blocks there all along. When we understand this and let go of it, it can finally let go of us, and we are free of our root of fear.

For me, fear was my ivy that anger was concealing. For others it will be deep-seated feelings which prevent the uncovering of the truth that blocks surrender. This may include despair, anxiety, or disillusion. With inner work and conscious breathing, particularly conscious connected breathing, you will uproot it. After years of meditation and reflection, conscious connected breathing finally got me there.

For now, my ivy of fear has been surrendered. It will return in some guise, and when it does, I hope to be present enough to take just one conscious breath. I will continue to struggle and need to surrender it. But now the sapling of self is free to flourish and bloom as nature intended. Nothing is blocking its path; 'I can't' has finally been replaced with 'I can'.

○ Let's breathe

Breathing space	The Fearless Breath
Duration	60 seconds
Response	To become aware of the storm we are in and try to settle it
Suited to	Adults, and for those who have worked with a breathworker
Best for	Emotional tsunami
Outcome	Restored hope and perspective

Set an intention that you want to get to the root of strong emotions that have been affecting everything. Bring these to a qualified breath worker – the GPBA (Global Professional Breathwork Alliance) is a good source to find one. Once you feel supported and safe in the relationship through a series of six to ten conscious connected breathing (CCB) sessions, you will get to the root of the issue. But it comes with a health warning: it is such a powerful and transformative tool that it is vital you feel safe and supported when doing it.

The joy of this breath is that once gained, our awareness is never lost; you can reconnect with the freedom you have reached at the end of six to ten sessions of CCB by taking just one minute of connected, flowing breath.

Breathe.

Chapter 11

In Our Flow

To be authentic is to be true. To let it all happen naturally from there is flow.

Gabor Maté refers to *here* as 'being plugged into our inner GPS and navigating life from there'.[12] The navigation is our flow. It is like a driver on a familiar journey arriving at their destination unaware of the places en route. Flow comes from an inner spaciousness when the doer just *is* and infuses what they are doing with their being. Anything that is copied is done solely with the thinking mind which, by its nature, is unoriginal.

I'm particularly taken by the creative process. The liquid moves of a dancer appear effortless, as if they are floating on water. When I built a house in the mountains, I was mesmerised by the ancient bog oak piled up in a nearby bog. I spent hours with it, uncovering the natural shapes that lay deep in their core. I try to be in flow and let things come from there, through the artist's body. The first draft of this book back in the day was done entirely old school: in longhand with a depleted Bic pen, a writing pad, and an old wooden desk. It felt more authentic and kinaesthetic, even if it was so much slower that way.

If we think about something truly creative, it is free, original, and largely unadorned by what's gone before. Artists seem to be hardwired to create and it enables them to be deeply in touch with who they are and to become themselves in the expression. But when artists stop being in flow, it can be as if they have pressed the pause button as they re-encounter their living world. This may be a world of anxiety and worry. Flow keeps the mind identification with these mind-made states at bay, but outside of the period of creation, they flood back in. The process of flow for the artist is like the role of the mantra for the meditator. This is explored in the next three examples.

A neighbour is a very keen painter and in retirement has a growing following of supporters and buyers. He spoke of the period of painting not as no-mind but as a time when the thoughts and worries of the day were kept at bay. And if he does have thoughts when painting, they are largely expressed in the form of shape or colour.

I have a close friend, a sculptor, who when working can go for long periods of time with no thought; he says he just tries to give what he is doing in the moment the dignity it deserves. He is in flow at these times and remains there for sustained periods. When he stops work, he can have less access to this flow state. Although artists have a ready opportunity to work from flow, we are all no different; when we lack access to flow states, life can be less enriching and more of an uphill climb.

My partner is a pianist and tells of the time that she practises as a meditation. A time when all thoughts drop away and the natural joy and exuberance of playing music become alive and euphoric within her. During this time, she becomes the muse and music. This can carry over to adjacent periods of non-playing, so a kind of mind decluttering and intuitive space occurs from playing.

Working from a state of flow is something magical, and possible. It's like stillness in a state of meditation. Here the mind is stilled in the process of creation, enabling the creativity of the heart to be heard and to flow. So when the mind is still, flow flows from our heart. It's accessible to all of us if we let it. And rather like a mantra which helps us to observe thought, perhaps there are three corresponding states of flow in the process of creating. Initially the creating focuses our mind on the process, and then insulates us from extraneous thought until such a time that we break free of everything and just allow the work to develop, unfold and become.

○ Let's breathe

Breathing space	The Flow Breath
Duration	60 seconds
Response	To breathe smoothly in flow
Best for	Co-creating, collaboration, creating, and connection
Outcome	Revived spirit; reconnecting with 'I am'

Our breath doesn't just follow our emotions and feelings – it also leads them. Activate your flow breath by doing something creative. Write a poem, paint a canvas, or grab a yarn of wool and decide to knit. Now, observe your breathing. If you observe your breathing when in a state of flow, you will see that it too will flow and be rounded and smooth, mirroring your flow state. If you consciously focus on the flow of your breath, it will help to lead to a flow state.

Breathe.

Chapter 12

Emanation Doesn't Do Drama

Eknath Easwaran, in his commentary of the Bhagavad Gita, comments that we all have a God seed within us.[13]

Just as a plant grows into its true potential from a tiny seed, we do too. Our job on the spiritual path is to prepare the ground of ourselves so the seed can just get on with it. The preparation is about understanding that we are not on the surface of our lives, and we are not our egos. When we know ourselves beyond the surface, we give room for the roots of our God seed to sprout. Once it starts to sprout it is unstoppable.

The process of sprouting is natural. We are just being us. When we are unadorned, we are in being. Here we emanate positivity because we are leading our life authentically. Being, not doing, is our authentic state and our true destiny. It is such a positive state that it becomes attractive to life and to others and things start to flow. In Daoist texts this is known as 'Wu Wei' or 'positive non-action.'[14]

This full embracing of our authentic selves and getting our false selves or egos out of the way creates the conditions for emanation.

Emanation in its truest sense is individuals being in their own life flow and radiating that. We just *are*; we know we are and live life from here with one voice. This is the voice of our being. When everything is coherent, we no longer need to keep having a row with ourselves. We are clear and the way is clear, and we communicate this to the outside world. With clarity we become more authentic and things start to fall into our lap as if by chance. We seem to keep getting lucky. Except it is not chance – it is flow. When we stop resisting, things happen. It's like all our life ducks get in a row. This is because when we just are, we reduce the internal obstacles and are in our natural state. These may not be the things that the ego projects as part of our identity but rather, they are what we are attracting to ourselves. Like goes to like. Positivity leads to positivity. Now that is not to say life becomes a breeze; we will continue to have difficulties or troubles. But we do not compound our problems by turning them into a drama and getting up on the stage of our life, re-enacting them for any like-minded soul prepared to listen.

Drama is in the opposite direction. It is ego appealing to ego. Emanation is being in our life flow – it is peaceful, it doesn't do drama. It just *is* and is our being responding to universal being or source energy. It is where the pilgrim and the path are one.

Attention is a key driver in life. We seek it out. Sometimes we create or re-enact drama to get it. But when we are not captivated by the social drug of attention, we pause the spin on things that keep turning the steering wheel of the bus. We care less about what people say. Flow is when our attention gets the right attention and when our being attracts similar energy. With heightened awareness you steer free of drama. Anyone who creates drama is creating the conditions that they know best to get the attention they so crave. But this is ego and can only attract ego. Like goes to like. Avoid these situations as people will be spinning away trying to build momentum for their egocentric worldview.

Instead look out for the radiators you will know then as you yourself become one. Like goes to like. When we are in being, we emanate being and so attract it. We become being magnets, just like some of the neurodivergent pupils I worked with. Here we are our best selves and role models. It is our natural state and is irresistible to life. At this point, things flow into our lives that are intended for us. Nothing needs to be forced. Try not trying. Better still, don't try not trying. Don't create the conditions for a row with yourself. Just be. When you are here you have created the ideal conditions for your God seed to grow. So in a sense, once we have got ourselves out of the way, all we have to do is let life get on with it – we let our God seed become.

◯ Let's breathe

Breathing space	The Seed Breath
Duration	60 seconds
Response	To know my God seed and trust in the process of my flowering
Suited to	Seekers of truth
Best for	When we need inspiration and encouragement
Outcome	Revived spirit; reconnecting with source energy

Try one fully conscious breath now and rest quietly in the space after the exhale. Really rest there. This is your being in your own ground.

When you are here, ask yourself these questions: 'What

does the universe want me to be? What beautiful flower or helpful crop is to emerge from my God seed?' Set your intention to find the answer and once found, to follow and serve it. Wait for the answer. This is who you most truly are and following it is what will make you most truly happy. This is your freedom and destiny.

As with all big questions, don't nag or badger your host. Especially when your host is the energy of the universe. Don't worry – it has heard. It has known the answer way before you knew the question but could only reveal it when you were ready. So just ask once or twice. It has heard you. Let go and trust. In the letting go and trusting, the answer will come. But if we nag, we create the conditions within us when we return to ego, and we have lost trust and so will block flow.

Breathe.

Part 2

Rest in Being

Awakening then is to wake up to the limitation of our mind and to see the potential of leading our lives from the energy of our heart. We have found our God seed. Our worldly parcel is more understood for what it is. We are now ready for the great growth which happens in the uncovering or letting go.

The whole process is as simple as putting our God seed in soil and sunlight, watering it occasionally and then letting nature get on with it. But don't worry – if you neglect it or forget about it, once started, growth is unstoppable. The only thing that you can influence now is the speed of growth. You do this simply by providing supportive conditions for growth. Just one conscious breath is enough.

This chapter is about breathing that breath and the great unwrapping that follows. We encourage our God seed by trusting and surrendering to its gentle inevitable unfolding.

Chapter 13

Surrendering With One Conscious Breath

Surrender is no walk in the park.

There, I said it. It is one of the more difficult concepts to grasp, and to breathe. Well, it was for me. But it can be mastered and embraced with the breath. So, in the following chapters, my understanding of surrender will continue to be accompanied by exercises or breathing spaces, which will try help to embody new learning at an experiential level.

With awakening, our body can start to relax because it does not have to be hyper-reactive to everything going on. We are on the way to the holy grail of relaxed attention. Deep bodily relaxation is the movement of surrender and its energy is freed up by the exhale, which is like sliding home to our truest self. Our exhale is an emptying and a letting go and a trust that all will continue to be well in that process. And so it will, just as night follows day, inhale turns to exhale. This rhythm of letting go frees us of the need to find a solution in the here and now.

Growing up I had a friend who I teased a little at the time because he would say he would sleep on something and get back to me. He would be very amused to hear that he is being spoken of on the same page as a Pope. Famously he even slept on the offer of a ticket to see Carlos Santana at the Hammersmith Odeon. He was the only one who acted in this way. He was extremely popular because he would always come back with a solid, reasoned and committed response. He remains unchanged in this regard and is the loving, quiet rock that so many of us turn to for advice and support.

When we don't know the answer to a problem, it's an opportunity to let go of this need to know, and to fix it, and instead give time and space to sort it all out. Far from being a problem, it's very positive to recognise that we do not know the answer and we wait and trust that it will emerge. The waiting and trusting is a preliminary sign of surrender – we are putting our faith in something way beyond the power of our conscious minds and implicitly acknowledging its limitations.

There is freedom and pleasure when we speak to someone who embodies this and who is open to the possibility of not knowing. Following a significant question, sometimes the best answer is to say, 'I don't know', and wait in that unknowing until a response emerges. This also gives space to take a conscious breath and open our wisdom gap. Doing this gives permission and space for the unconscious mind, to come in and sort it all out.

In creating this space, we acknowledge and tap into our innate capacity for wisdom and trust in its source. Pope St John XIII famously surrendered everything and finished his nightly prayers with: 'Well, I did my best. It's your church so I'm going to bed now.'[15]

○ Let's breathe

Breathing space	The Wisdom of the Heart Breath
Duration	One minute
Response	To reframe a problem and create inner space for a quiet resolution
Best for	Uncertainty and discernment
Outcome	To hear the wisdom of our heart

Know that your wisest self is deep inside you beyond the busyness of the thinking mind, and when you ask for an answer from your heart, it will come. It may not come instantly, but it will come. So only ask once or twice. Have faith in the process – invite but don't nag. Remember, to nag is to communicate a lack of faith, and our ego is back in.

Set an intention, such as by the end of this breath you would like a new way of looking at or understanding an issue. Seeing a problem in a new way is the first step to resolving it in a new way. Breathe using conscious connected breathing for just one minute. And wait. Know that what comes up following your request and your quiet is the voice of your heart. Once you have looked at the issue from this place, you have changed the energy around it and have set up the conditions for its resolution.

Sit comfortably, set your intention, breathe, and wait. Then wait some more if you need to. The more you practise, the more you will hear. Your inner voice will become clearer – follow this voice whenever you can.

Chapter 14

The Difficulties
of Letting Go

Churchill, the British Prime Minister during World War II, understood how to use the new medium of radio. His most famous speech ended with the rousing statement, almost as a grand finale, 'We will never surrender.'[16] This was a landmark and was taken to heart by the British and their allies.

There is a generation of older British citizens, women in particular, who are extremely resilient. They are like the young Churchill brides of the '30s and '40s. They lived through the war and seem to have carried the same 'we will never surrender' attitude into their old age. This particularly shows itself in the illnesses and ailments that now accompany many of them. Some carry on as if through sheer determination and willpower they will 'see this one off'. Although incredibly admirable, it is not always easy for them as there can be very little headspace to let go. I grew up in this atmosphere and on some level absorbed the lesson deeply, and it has taken many years to come to understand. Psychologically, maybe I am a Churchill baby.

My parents both survived the Second World War and had stories about sleeping overnight in the London Underground. There were times when it was too dangerous to leave the house and they had to stay in a personal Anderson bomb shelter quickly assembled under the kitchen table. My mother, just nine years old at the time, was allowed one luxury, usually her doll, to accompany her. Rather like the way we count the gap between lightning flashes and thunder rolls to know how safe we are, they would count the time from a burst of light to a physical explosion to know how far the bombs were away. They were told to be brave and that they would be fine.

Our personality, habits and conditioning limit our ability to surrender – mine especially. I made a commitment to get up early every morning before work to write this book. Commitments can be all-consuming for me, and I can become a bit obsessive this way. Hands up, this is one of my more neurodivergent-type behaviours. We see this behaviour a lot with neurodivergent children. It manifests itself in an obsessive need to finish a task before moving on, or when following a rigid timetable where the sequence of events must happen in predictable order. It's not always healthy for children and it's not always healthy for me.

There is a resilience here that can seem brave but can also be understood as a form of resistance. Our elders supressed the need to release, to let go and let be. They remained busy in doing and sometimes built an identity around the virtue of this.

The breath that symbolises letting go is a sigh. We are hardwired to sigh quite a bit, but it has negative social connotations so we often find ourselves suppressing it. This is a beautiful sound of surrender and should never be suppressed. Don't suppress surrender, don't suppress a sigh – let it go and be grateful. When you hear yourself sigh, realise that your body is wise. Your body understands, but your brain doesn't

– which is why we struggle with surrender. Our brain wants to stay in control and does this by judging and rationalising all thoughts that come its way. Pause. Just go with it, let go, surrender and be. When we surrender, we are in the present moment and there is nothing to resist.

Resistance comes from our ego holding onto positions. It cannot coexist with surrender because surrender lets go of everything in the present moment. True surrender trumps the ego. Conscious breathing gives us the courage and insight to uncover this magnificent truth; that is the essence of who we truly are: a surrendered being living from our heart.

☾ Let's breathe

Breathing space	The Coming Home Breath
Duration	60 seconds
Response	To trust in the flow
Best for	Times of fear and feeling blocked
Outcome	Reconnecting with your curious, vulnerable inner child

Breathe consciously to a ratio of 1:2. Inhale for a count of four and exhale for a count of eight. Four in, eight out. When we elongate the exhale, we let go more fully. The importance of consciously sighing has already been written about.

Do this for a minute. On a ratio of 4:8, that's five breaths in total. If you really want to ground and embody this breath, don't count but use your heartbeat as your source and coordinate with that. Four beats in, eight beats out. Four beats in, eight beats out. And so on.

Return to this in times of resistance and take conscious sighs through the day.

Breathe, rest in being.

Chapter 15

The Stone Wall

Last night I noted my intention to write about my experience of building a stone wall and linking it to self-identity.

Noting an intention at night before sleep gives the unconscious mind the opportunity to sort it out. Sometimes trust in a process is as important as the outcome. This happened here.

Our home is suburban on the edge of Dublin. The garden is quite small and walled, and although overlooked has a sense of containment and privacy. With a friend over the summer, we have been working on the process of clearing out old plants and equipment and adding raised beds. The project started with the removal of an old unused trampoline and basketball net with a stand. They had had their day and were taking up a lot of space. Gardens need decluttering too.

In a contained garden, adding levels interrupts the visual flow to the walls and gives a sense of depth and space. We incorporated three levels in this way. Yesterday, we started the final project: a raised flower bed where the trampoline was. The retaining wall which will contain the new soil is made from sandstone. Over the years I have got to know a quarry owner in the Slieve Bloom Mountains in the heart of Ireland, who is happy for us to gather a pile of stones and charges us accordingly. If he isn't there, we send him a photo of the pile and he responds, 'Sure, you will always bump into me in the village to sort it out.' There is a reason why so many people have settled happily in Ireland and call it home.

Back to the wall. There are two ways to make a stone wall. We can look at the space in the wall and try and find a stone to fit – the 'mind the gap' approach. Or we can pick up the stone and find a home for it. The first way the wall is the source and focus, and the second way the stone is. We take the first approach because it helps to see the wall evolve. If we judge a gap wrongly, we can always adapt the stone a little with a diamond-tipped disc cutter which, with every adaptation, sends a plume of stone dust into the air.

This morning when I went out, there was a fine spray of dust. It was most clearly seen on the glass top of our garden table. The glass reflected the situation, revealing a lot of dust and spaces between it. I wondered if we asked the stone wall at this point, 'What are you?', what the answer would be.

Would it say: 'I am a fine stone wall, holding up this lovely, raised bed of flowers. I am made from Slieve Bloom sandstone carefully collected in the quarry in Clonaslee and brought to Dublin in three carloads. I was envisioned by Michael and built with friends. I was lovingly made with nine rows of slim sandstone built in the shape of a slow curve. You can sit on me and see the flower bed close up. Look, you can see that now. This is what I am.' Here we have a stone wall proudly identifying with its history, form, and function. Or would it say, 'Do you see that dust and space? I am that in my essence.'

So it is with us and our self-identity. If we identify with our history, form, and function, we become like the proud stone wall. But if we see the space and dust that we are made of, we see the *no-thing* of us, and of everything. A deeper question yet becomes, is our self-identity a stone, or a non-stone identity? Attach yourself to the stone identity and you can be lost in the world of form and clutter. But by identifying with the non-stone identity you see the essence in everything. When we know ourselves and others from this place, the truth sets us free.

◯ Let's breathe

Breathing reflection

Asking a question of our unconscious mind is a great way to find solutions. I do this before sleep, as in this example. Just ask yourself a question and let your unconscious take over. Sometimes when you wake you will have an answer. A friend of mine, an avid reader, throws books on the floor for the number of problems he wants to resolve. When he wakes, they serve as physical prompts to uncover. Similarly, we can ask ourselves a question before we take a conscious breath. Questions like, 'What is being asked of me here?' or 'What should I say now?'

By giving space and the breath, we open the possibility of finding the answer. This is a great way of letting go of attachment to current mind-centred solutions. Don't demand an answer; that is like an annoying voice in the back of our head repeating, 'Are we there yet?' Instead, just sow a questioning seed, wait, and trust. Do this now. Breathe. Rest in being. Repeat whenever you can. And wait.

Breathe, rest in being.

Chapter 16

Knowing the Ground of our Mind

It is important to prepare the ground of our minds with care, and to be vigilant to external influences.

When it is built, the new raised bed will be filled with soil. This is being taken from around the garden and combined with new topsoil and well-rotted farmyard manure. Bark mulch will be placed at the bottom of the bed. This will rot down to provide nutrients to the low-lying roots of a ginkgo biloba tree that the raised bed incorporates. We consciously prepare the ground of the raised bed in the same way that we consciously prepare the ground of our mind. If we are not awake during this, weeds will blow in from unknown and unwanted sources and all the flower beds in the neighbourhood will start to look the same.

Similarly, we need to be careful how we consciously plant the raised bed of the mind and surround it with positive and supportive sources. If we remain unconscious throughout, unwanted seeds will also blow in and take over.

Both the raised bed and our mind are places where we can make conscious decisions about what we do. Once the ground of the raised bed is prepared, it is ready for planting. And once the ground of our mind is uncluttered and free, our God seed can take root and will flower as nature intended.

With awareness we become more aware of the societal agenda, or profit, that so many groups and organisations have in keeping us unconscious, and our raised beds identical. We see how their messages are always there, like the seeds of adjacent weeds, ready to grow and take hold in the fertile ground of an unconscious mind.

Our mind loves a habit because it is predictable and through repetition sustains the illusion that it is in control. Knowing this, we can beat it by its own game by developing a practice that nourishes our heart – whether it's something like reflective prayer, meditation, Tai Chi or yoga – because when the mind gets its habit, it doesn't object, *and so it backs off, giving time and space for our heart to develop.*

For some neurodivergent children, the mind's desire for habit is equally strong. They can latch onto something seemingly innocuous, in the distant past, which can grow into an unexplained source of repetitive patterns of behaviour. These can become numerous and unpredictable. I have seen these include things as diverse as the need to watch a certain video before doing something, travelling exclusively in certain lanes on the motorway, or spinning around three times prior to passing through a doorway. Behaviours like this help create some order in what can be perceived as a chaotic and overwhelming world.

Supporting this is a painstaking job and everyone in the child's life needs to be on the same page – and the rest of us are no different. We too need to be accountable to a community or group of people that keep us on track. This helps us to stay awake and safeguards us against our unhelpful behaviours becoming ingrained and repeated.

The concept of awakening is hardly new; over two thousand five hundred years ago, Socrates warned the citizens of Athens not to sleepwalk through their lives. When we are awake, we understand that surrendering to the flow of life is the primary fruit of this awakening. Here we emanate truth and positivity and attract like-minded people, and soon things begin to grow and multiply because other people join, and a virtuous cycle of positivity evolves.

Some people when they wake up to the external influences that have been driving them for so long can go off-grid altogether and retreat from the world. I understand this because in retrospect I did it for a while. Generally though, we need to return, and the hardest role is to remain conscious among the distraction and noise of our modern world. Equally, when we return from a period of reflection, retreat or withdrawal from the busyness of our lives, the intention is to try to bring the calm centre with us. This can get quickly overlooked in the hustle and bustle of life.

With awakening, we know that when our body is calm and peaceful it's because our mind is calm and is leading the way home. A calm, clear, awakened mind is pure and simple. It is the source of our relaxed attention. In its uncluttered simplicity it is available to hear the wiser messages of our heart. There is no resistance and nothing getting in the way. This calm, clear mind guided home by a loving heart is our life journey.

But how do we maintain a calm, clear mind in the chaos? The first thing is to flip this coin too, and see the benefit of distraction, as it provides so many opportunities for practice and return. Then try to remain steady in the chaos: consciously breathe and connect with the flow of the outer world from your inner calm, from your heart.

Your home is where your heart is. And the sound of it, the sound of 'home' is like the Indian root mantra, 'aum' (om). Repeating this for millennia has brought faithful meditators home to their heart. Just one fully conscious breath also brings you home. Home to your heart. *Om.*

◐ Let's breathe

Breathing space	The Calm and Centred Breath
Duration	60 seconds
Response	To hear my true self and filter out false distractions
Suited to	Busy minds; high-level executives; parents and caretakers
Best for	Claustrophobic train rides; during the workday; low energy
Outcome	Seeing the perfect white lotus flower of self again

Let go with the breath and return home to yourself. As you exhale, repeat the word 'home'. Try to hear three sounds on the exhale, */h/ /oo/ /mmm/,* just like the three syllables in the Indian root mantra, 'aum'.

Do this a few times now and whenever you get the chance to remember. Then wait and hear the silence at the end. This is when we rest in being.

Breathe, rest in being.

Chapter 17

The Sounds of Silence

To fully know and appreciate something at a physical level, we first have to know and experience its opposite.

To truly appreciate being pain-free, we will have experienced pain; to appreciate our abundance, we need to have had feelings of lack; and in the earlier example of the neighbour's burglar alarm, we appreciate silence on the other side of the sound pounding in our head.

Similarly, there is something magical about listening to live music after the pandemic. I was at a concert very recently where everyone sat in silent appreciation as music filled the concert hall. We were still, part of a listening community, supporting the musicians and one another in an unspoken communion. There were no words to attend to so we could simply wait, listen, and be inspired. After the first piece, some of the orchestra left and the stage was rearranged for the string section to perform a new contemporary composition by a young Bulgarian composer.

The soloist was a young cellist playing on a four-hundred-year-old Stradivari violin loaned from a musical foundation. The foundation enables soloists to play priceless, timeless instruments and the anonymous benefactor gets a sense that they are contributing to something very rare and beautiful. They may have been in the audience; we will never know – such is the beauty of this quiet musical gift. The nature of the exchange is a bit like an intergenerational process of pass the parcel with each person contributing to the layers, or patina, rather than removing them.

Irish audiences are renowned by musicians the world over for their generosity and warmth. The composer came from Bulgaria for the recital and went on stage to greet her friend and fellow Bulgarian conductor. What happened next was pure spontaneous joy. Everyone who played, and everyone who listened, just let go once the piece dropped away into an ecstatic silence. At the interval, I squeezed my way through the row of seats. An older lady remained in her seat, physically frail, and with a light and luminous spirit within, turned to me and said:

Wow, just wow, there is no more, that was just wonderful.
I looked at her and smiled and nodded as I in turn could add no words or emotions to that. These peak experiences timelessly seed our conscious mind and can be an ongoing source of joy.

The final piece was more traditional, by Tchaikovsky. The second movement ended as it began with a contracted stillness and silence, the animation of the conductor settled and stilled as she led the orchestra into the final deep silence. Her outer stillness now emanating the gap, the 'no music' in the music. It was as if the music was to bring us there to this point of no music, a poignant and universal experience of silence. Without music, we would not be able to fully hear the silence. In retrospect, this musical silence was met by the audience members' stillness, and pure peace and joy flowed.

Daoists speak of this kind of listening as sacred hearing. Here the heart gives attention to an emptiness as the source of everything. This is a listening of the spirit in which all the senses are open and empty. Only by the emptiness of all our senses within can the whole being listen. This is a deep hearing, which can never be heard by the ear or the mind alone. It is a wisdom of 'those who know not, yet being empty, carry a full light'.[17]

Silence and stillness are no-thing. Silence refers more to the outer world of form and experience, and stillness is more of an inner dimension reflecting the stilling of the mind and the associated thought stream. When the no-thing, the silence, of the concert hall meets the no-thing, the stillness, within us, we are in a timeless state of pure joy and peace. In the words of the lady in the audience, we reach the place of *wow, just wow* – where *there is no more*.

When we surrender, we don't need to force anything, just let go. As we let go we start to begin to sense the unfathomable spaciousness of the no-thing that contains everything. From this space we flow with the magnetic energy of love.

☾ Let's breathe

Breathing space	The 'Wow, Just Wow' Breath
Duration	60 seconds
Response	To appreciate the beauty and wonder we are contained in now
Suited to	The artists at heart
Best for	Reimagining and inspiring us after falling asleep
Outcome	Revived spirit; an appreciation of wonder; finding the awe in awesome

Whenever I am aware of my thoughts during a concert, I try to visualise the conductor and bring my mind back to sync, back to no thoughts, to no-thing. The best way for me is through conscious breathing, often returning to one conscious breath. When I am trying to walk a tightrope of no-thing, I use Coherent Breathing (p267). It's simply a way of inhaling and exhaling evenly through the nose once every ten to twelve seconds. I keep doing this methodically as if walking along a narrow mountain ridge of now, with distractions on either side.

Find yourself a piece of music. Something instrumental and uncluttered is ideal. An acoustic guitar, solo cello, or piano works for me. You can also listen to the human voice in a form that doesn't require you to process language. Just be with that music. Consciously breathe. Breathe into the silence and spaces and as you continue, feel yourself inspired as if directly breathing in the music through your nose and letting it go. Finding yourself consciously breathing to music, especially live music, is a wonderful place to be. It is the place you seek, where mind, body, soul and spirit surrender.

Breathe, rest in being.

Chapter 18

Breathing Through the Stuff of Life

Our life is here now up on the ledge of this precious present moment. It all happens here and now.

What has been and gone has been and gone, and what will be will be. The only way we can cope with our past is to be here now and breathe life and understanding into it. Just as the only way we cope with our future is to be here now, in flow now, and let our future flow. We do this by getting ourselves, or rather our false selves, which is our identification with our thoughts and our ego, out of the way. When we do this, things become aligned. It's a bit like instead of our life being a heap of iron filings, it becomes a positive series of them aligning together from our magnetic heart centre. Filing to filing to filing. Now to now to now. This neverending chain of 'right now' moments is the flow of love in our life.

But despite this understanding and positivity, life will keep happening and what happens will be like a broken record until we get the hint, lift the stylus and start the next track. In doing this we take the learning that is required from the situation and move on. Once we finally respond to what is in front of us now rather than react to it, we have lifted the stylus and are ready to move onto the next problem.

The problems we are presented contain the lessons we most need to learn. If we keep receiving the same problems, we are stuck in a groove, and will probably remain there until we resolve the issue. Once we learn, we are ready to move on and it is likely that we will be presented with a new set of learning through a new set of problems. Our learning and our heart deepen in this way. This is a positive cycle of feedback and reinforcement from life. We keep growing through the problems that arise. This is like a present-moment cycle of karma. From goodness now, goodness flows now. But the opposite is also the case. From ignorance or reaction now, further ignorance or reaction will follow.

So respond to a situation and you will grow and move onto another one – positivity leading to positivity – but react to it and it will keep going round, coming back to bite you until you learn to respond. In the famous quote by Rita Mae Brown but often misattributed to Albert Einstein, 'the definition of insanity is doing the same thing over and over and expecting different results.'[18]

The central theme of this book is that we gain freedom when we move from reaction to response by taking just one conscious breath. In taking the breath prior to responding, we massively alter our life outcomes now and in the future moments that flow from now. By consciously breathing, our iron filings of events are no longer in a heap; they are in alignment and in flow.

To grow up is to psychologically grow up and make adult responses. Here we see the big picture because we know of our ego and understand our past and how it has conditioned us. We do not need to transcend it, just know it fully and unconditionally accept where we are now. In this acceptance we stop the process of endlessly recycling past issues, we get down from the sorry-go-round, and we open up the possibility of being free here now.

As a grown-up though, we still have our inner child with us. It is a great blessing, our sensitive and vulnerable inner little one which needs to be minded by us in a grown-up way. Our child is a curious vulnerable artist and playmate that needs protection from a cynical mindset that can shut it down with a few misdirected thoughts or words. Becoming an adult, we become authentic and parent ourselves, or rather, we parent our inner child. But this grown-up self-parenting style does not come with a lifetime warranty. We all hope to reach physical adulthood, but it's not guaranteed that we get there psychologically, even less so spiritually. For me, psychological adulthood came ridiculously late. It was in my mid-forties, and it was around the time I handled the really complicated stuff that life was presenting me with.

Ram Dass said, if you think you are enlightened, go and spend a week with your parents.[19] That's certainly a sign of our spiritual evolution. I think we could also say, if you think you are psychologically grown-up, go and sort out their conflicting care needs as they age.

Many people loved Dad – he made us laugh and had a very kind heart. One day shortly after arriving from my home in Dublin, I got in the front door to see my mum pushing Dad, who by this stage was very frail with advanced dementia, up the stairs. He could no longer do it alone, and in the absence of any hoists, her slight physical frame was all the lifting they had. Mum categorically didn't want help and didn't welcome any intrusion. But the situation had gone too far, and deep down she knew she needed it – she just wasn't ready. Later we rang around and we found a suitable nursing home to visit. Luckily, they could see Dad the next day. The timing was tight as I was flying home a few days later. That afternoon, we both understood in terms of their safety, we had two choices: either Mum took the help, or we drove Dad together to the nursing home the following day.

Given the options, Mum went for the help. The whole family breathed again. That was my first adult breath, forty-six years after my initial one. How's that for slow learning? I finally got there with two defining breaths: the first of discernment that helped see the situation clearly with the action to take, and the second a huge sigh of surrender and relief. These big life decisions are multifaceted and need to be done consciously. When making a tough life decision consciously, we must ask ourselves: 'Am I exercising unnecessary force (which would be the ego), or is this truly what the situation requires (which is consciousness or love)?'

○ Let's breathe

Breathing reflection

This is a very useful way of discerning the fork in the road as life presents itself to us.

What big stuff is in front of you today? What would the situation look like if you brought a little perspective and space to it? Breathe into it now. Having done this, what is the most conscious way ahead? Project yourself into a time when you have made the decision.

Sigh. Sigh again.

Having breathed to discern one side of your action and breathed again to let go on the other, you have added breath bookends to it. Ask yourself, 'How do I feel now?' If you feel relaxed and content, your body is probably telling you this is a wise course of action. If you feel tense and not at peace, your body may be telling you something else.

Breathe, rest in being.

Chapter 19
Fear

'In the cave you fear to enter lies the treasure you seek.'

– Joseph Campbell

Linked to the previous chapter is our fear. But whereas in the previous chapter we act, here we fight, freeze or run away.

Fear prevents us from acting because we don't know what we don't know, but even when we do know, we might not know why we are holding back. And sometimes even when we know, we are unable to act because it's just too big and overwhelming to get our head around. In fear we can feel so overcome and alone and unsupported.

There is an old saying: there are two ways to become unhappy. The first way is to not get what you want, and the second way is to get it. Once we are wishing with our minds, we are not accepting what *is*. When this happens, we are trying to control the flow of our life and so making our impressions through a kind of unexamined fear.

Fear at its most profound is the absence of love. More accurately still, fear is identifying so fully with the thoughts in our head that they block and mask our love. In the human heart, love shows in many ways, which include faith, hope, joy, loyalty, unconditional friendship, courage, and support. The voice of love is the quiet steadfast encouragement of the way ahead. It is the sound of truth. Sometimes we take our learning from the unlikeliest of sources. So let's talk about banks and love. Increasingly, banks warn us of fraudsters by saying that they would never ring or contact us in ways that compromise our online safety or security. Did you know that it's a bit like that with our heart? It will never contact us through our ego, or shout, or put our security in jeopardy. Instead, it murmurs quietly in our centre. We know it is the voice of our truth because hearing it makes us feel safe, joyful and peaceful. It is the voice we invited in the wisdom gap breath earlier.

In fear we can't always easily hear the right voice, and if we can, we may not be free to listen. That's because when we are in fear, we are unwittingly stuck in ego, and if we can't see beyond the pervasive identification with our ego and our egoic relationships, we are unavailable to hear the authentic voice of our true selves.

Because we identify with what we think, we are cut off from our being and so are contained by our fear. We become cut off from our love. Fear blocks us from our authenticity and truth and prevents us from taking the steps that we need to take, to embrace who we truly are. We can't see the wood for the trees, and are not ready to go with the flow of love that leads us home to ourselves because the presence of egoic fear is blocking us.

Yet we are never cut off – we just think we are because we are captivated by our thoughts. In breathing the fear, we blow away our captivation with thoughts, and give ourselves the space and realisation to be here now, and to hear the voice of love here now.

Once the thinking mind has been developed, we have no choice but to move forward. It's a bit like the central idea in Michael Rosen's famous children's book, *We're Going on a Bear Hunt*:

>*We can't go over it (any obstacle on our path),*
>
>*We can't go under it (any obstacle on our path),*
>
>*We just have to go through it...*
>
>*...I'm not scared.*[20]

Except on this grown-up journey there are no bears on our path. All the obstacles in our way are of our own making and exist in the mind. We can't get over the mind with the mind, we can't go under the mind with it – we just have to get through the mind with no-mind. The only way through is to surrender with no-mind to reach universal truth. We can only see the truth with our being, which is our love.

If the only way over or under is through, then what we go through can be a stumbling block. Especially if we have followed the socially conditioned life script up until now and things may have been good to us on the surface (as it was in my case). Why would we transcend something we have aspired to for so long? The reason is because our ultimate purpose in life is to overcome our deepest fears, and become authentic and be in the flow of our life from there. Simply put we must free ourselves up so we can learn to love fully. If we are lucky, life will take on whatever disruptive force is needed for us to get there and make us surrender to the truth. If it doesn't, we can get a bit stuck in our groove, just like that old-fashioned stylus on a broken record.

For many, seeing this happens when we die. Death is the ultimate roll call of the ego and for some, the illusion holds out until then. But for others, the illusion breaks in life, and we see our egos and so can start to become free here now.

Some of the neurodivergent children I worked with didn't have the same need to be authentic. They were already there. But they too had a journey and oftentimes it was a different one. It was to get to the other side of the pain, confusion and misunderstanding of what could be seen as complex behaviour. Once the communication behind their behaviour was understood, they were more free to be themselves and had a greater chance to radiate their enormous capacity for peace and joy. Helping them get there was a complex privilege that motivated people to keep working alongside them. This relationship is a very healing one. At its simplest, we are waiting and helping them to transcend their behaviour, and they are waiting and helping us to transcend our thinking. When this happens, we have an authentic relationship for us both; we know of its authenticity because it brings about a real human connection now. It is love here now. It is that simple.

◖ Let's breathe

> **Breathing reflection**
>
> When we get in touch with ourselves at our deepest level, we meet our fear. Conscious connected breathing got me there. Further details of this are listed in the appendix (p258). For the moment, take a conscious breath. How are you breathing now?
>
> Breathe, rest in being.

Chapter 20

In Love With
the World

I have borrowed the title of a wonderful autobiography of awakening and surrender by Yongey Mingyur Rinpoche.[21]

As a revered Tibetan Lama he finds his authentic way the other side of the monastery walls and, in so doing, nearly dies, eventually to return in a whole new way. It is a wonderful message of how by facing into our biggest fears we encounter love.

Essentially there are two ways we can be in the world: we can operate from love or we can operate from fear. Actually erase that – let's go deeper still. In truth there is just one way. We can be in love with the world or not. Being in love with the world is connecting and surrendering to what is. Fear may feel real, as explored above, but it isn't an active state as such. It's the 'cannot' which holds us back. For Yongey Mingyur Rinpoche, his 'cannot' was the monastery walls.

Love is not what we have been led to believe it is. The notions of romantic love are outdated historical legacies around the need to turn sexual attraction into something more socially palatable and conditioned. Sex needed to be taken in by the Church and presented as something safer and more controllable in the fear that all authority and control would be lost. Shame around sinning was given to us by an external authority. In *A New Earth*, Eckhart Tolle writes that 'to sin means we miss the mark, as an archer who misses the target, so to sin means to miss the point of our existence.'[22] The only real sin is to be inauthentic and miss out on who we really are because here we miss out on our capacity to be in love with the world.

Don't label things and beat yourself up; life is hard enough without talk of sin. All we need to do is be our authentic selves and not miss our mark. Missing our mark is a place where we overlook our capacity for stillness and silence and the wonder-filled life that flows from it. When we miss our mark, we miss out on our fullness and our love.

Mutual love is when the stillness and spaciousness in one person respond and nurture these in another. Love is not a feeling; it is not work. Love is the acceptance that we *are*. It is the complete lack of judgement of who we are and from that space to see and embrace the other. It is the polar opposite of any notion of sin – because in sin we miss our mark.

In ego, we are blinkered in unknowing, which inhibits us and how we experience life, but in love our aim is true and there is no identification with this. A form of love that fosters personal growth happens in the workplace too. We show love to our colleagues when we inspire them and fully accept mistakes. This is an unconditional workplace.

Like the Buddhists define truth by what it is not with concepts such as emptiness, impermanence, and non-attachment, love too can be defined as what it is not. Love is not of the ego. To know love, we must know of our identification with the ego and walk in the opposite direction. Remember, ego is manifested in the pervasive and false identification states of worry, doubt, longing, desire, anger, a need to be right, a need to be wrong, a need to be this, a need to be that. Any need-to-be state is inauthentic. All the identities which derive from our busyness and distraction are from here, and they take us away from love. The ego resists being because when we are still and have a sense of our inner spaciousness, we start to see the truth and have its number.

When we know what love is not, we are more open to see what it is. Love is simple and authentic. It is what we are in our heart and it is what connects us all together and with the energy of everything. We are love and God is love. We are here so God can experience love through us in a way that is fully unique and fully human. If we do not live our life fully authentically, this opportunity is lost.

Egoic love is a double whammy because in being presented as a yearned-for solution, it obscures the truth. Egoic love is not love; it is the words we have put on chemistry and temporary mutual attraction. Love can come from egoic love when both parties have woken to the myth behind it and surrendered to the truth. In mutual surrender and understanding comes real love. In a way, the ego is quite benign as it has the potential for built-in obsolescence as it gets us into situations that will inevitably lead to pain and disappointment. Here we can finally recognise it and let go. So in this way, the notions of romantic love could be seen as a positive myth.

Parents of neurodivergent children can have a tough road from the outset. Not only the ongoing and lifelong physical, emotional, and financial difficulties of care and provision; in our society they often find themselves advocating and lobbying for resources which have not been given to them by right, all the while trying to come to terms with a diagnosis. The needs presented by the child can be so overwhelming that some parents do not have the bandwidth with all the busyness of the first two stages of endless caring and the need to advocate that they can be too busy, too burned out, and too distracted to reach acceptance. Paradoxically, all this conceals the wonderful opportunity that the children bring, which is to teach us to unconditionally surrender to the authenticity and truth that they are. This is their masterclass on love.

The demand for authenticity and truth can make or break parents and their relationships. It is hard to see how it would be otherwise. There is rarely a middle way. The light at the end of the tunnel comes with unconditional acceptance. This is not covered up with care or busyness – it is just a letting go of all previous assumptions to accept what *is*. It is the light at the end of the tunnel for the child too as in this acceptance they can fully be and are not met with any resistance. A relationship of truth and not the ego develops.

Resistance and disappointment are of the ego, and from this place we aren't available to see the truth, and are not ready to surrender to the huge potential for peace and joy that the child brings. I taught deaf students previously and when a parent heard their child was deaf, they were ready to listen. In accepting truth, everything flows.

But what of the child in all this? Life can be so incredibly challenging for them. They are sometimes unable to express their needs and wants, or to put words on pain or its source. Behaviour becomes a way to communicate, and because this is seen at face value, it gets misunderstood. Those of us experiencing the behaviour are on the outside looking in; do we really know what this is about? Perhaps what is being most deeply communicated is, 'this is what I am and what I really need is acceptance that it's okay.' When the time is right, with complete acceptance everything changes completely. The relationship becomes unconditional love and is a wonderful beacon of love for those of us fortunate to see it.

Neurodivergent children are ambassadors of the truth. We either see them and their behaviours and accept them for who they are, or we don't. For the child, acceptance is gold – they are no longer met with resistance of any form and now meet full acceptance. In this, they have taught us to love authentically. This is so much easier for the professional, who closes the door at the end of the day, than for the parent. But for everyone privileged to know the child, there is the potential for a significant growth path ahead as come what may, the child with all their authenticity will keep pushing at the door until we let go of our resistance and let them in.

This space of joint acceptance is love. We know how real it is by how diametrically opposed it is to romantic love. It is one of the quiet, socially unacknowledged jobs that neurodivergent children do – they teach us acceptance free of ego, and in that space, we learn to love authentically and unconditionally. This is the masterclass the families taught me.

It is in full acceptance of what's in front of us that we live our lives with acceptance, authenticity and love. When we need nothing other than what we have right now, we are beyond fear and can truly love. The greater the challenges, the greater the opportunities to accept and transcend them.

Cycling back now to fear and comparing it with love, we see that they are opposite sides of an incomplete circle, like a hooped earring. Love is total acceptance of what is, and fear is not. Love is in trust – fear is in worry. Love is of being – fear is of thought. Love is of today – fear is yesterday. Love is now – fear is tomorrow. We complete the circle when we put the earring on. Doing this we embody the possibilities and join together the loose ends to make the circle. We know now of fullness and contain everything that up to now we had understood to be opposite. In fear we are stuck at one end of the loop and cannot see the big picture – we cannot complete it with our love. Whereas in love everything is whole, clear and complete.

Consciously breathe now and reveal your inner stillness. That is your gateway to the source of love. Love and be loved from that space. How are you breathing now? Breathe. Rest in being. Smile and sigh.

Chapter 21

Please Fasten Your Seatbelts

Bord Fáilte (The Irish Tourist Board) might take issue, but taking off from the runway at Dublin Airport, the sky is often covered or densely patched with clouds.

As we take off, we pass through the clouds, and it is only after the ascent that the true nature of the blue sky can be seen. From here in the gap we can see our point of departure clearly. The mind is like this. Its natural state is blue-sky mind. Clouds pass but they are not the real landscape. They are temporary expressions of what comes and goes, and they temporarily obscure the eternal blue sky. From the plane, we can look down and see the ground below and look up into the sky and begin to understand the openness and vast spaciousness above. There are no clouds mediating the experience, distracting us from the vast, open blue sky. Simply observing the sky and letting the clouds pass undisturbed, we can understand the true nature of our mind.

With this renewed understanding, clouds are welcomed. They are not harbingers of rain or thoughts we must endlessly chase. They become our prompts of awakening. Given our sky in Ireland, we probably get more opportunities for this than pretty much any place else. Perhaps Bord Fáilte can turn our clouds into a unique billboard: 'Wake up with the clouds in Ireland.'

Once we have taken off and are cruising, all is well. The sky is blue, and the clouds are understood for what they are. But wait, we are thirty thousand feet up in the air and we still need to get down. Both the weather and the air traffic control must be clear for us to come into land.

Please fasten your seatbelts now because our inflight ego gets us twice. First it disguises the nature of the mind and secondly, in creating fear it generates its own obstacles for us to come into land. Travelling with our ego is a bit like flying long haul with our toddlers. Both can be difficult passengers – neither can be expected to be quiet and still – they would rather keep our attention by pressing the inflight call bell and getting up and down the aisle.

If the fear around our descent were translated to the cockpit, we would be stuck in space (until the jet fuel ran out). Imagine the plane circling the runway unable to ever get down. With each loop the untrained cockpit-mind would encounter another iteration of ego-fear blocking the descent. This is what our ego does in surrender; it turns our mind into fearful, untrained cockpit-mind. It wants to stay in control and will get up to every trick in the book to stop us coming into land. Don't let it call the shots – remember to just keep it in your pocket.

The role of the ego in the first instance is to keep us safe and it does this by remaining in control. As we begin to awaken, the ego will resist and persist to continually get us to buy into its perspective and understanding. The moment we start to see the truth and raise our inflight blinds, the ego is on the wane because it cannot exist in the light of truth. But before it does it will mutate and become subtler to catch us out.

Modern life is complicated and hectic. In busy family life we get all manner of opportunities to breathe and let go. Stuff just keeps happening! And it will keep happening until we get it and accept it. Have an image of yourself as a tree in a storm which remains rooted by being flexible. Embrace all with gratitude and acceptance. What happens happens. It is what we do with all this stuff that is the mark of our growth. See your distractions and troubles as just another opportunity to practise and go again. Another take-off and another landing. Be easy. Life often has other plans. Going with this, accepting fully what is in front of us, we bend in the storm. Bend because this stuff is what happens in the living of our life. This is enough. When we consciously bend in the storm, we go with our flow, knee deep in the flow of life.

Listening to some accomplished spiritual teachers is like watching them take off and land. When they speak to a large audience, a few things are apparent. Many start with a sigh of release and surrender to the message. Some are unprepared and talk from inner stillness. Frequently they talk very slowly and deliberately, attending to the space between the words which are as much a teaching as the words themselves. And finally, when an authentic teacher leaves the stage, they leave the teaching and land back into their own ordinary everyday life. There is no concept of the guru up there on stage. The teaching does not belong to anyone; it flows from consciousness, and it is life's teaching yearning for expression through them. The ego is absent, and this absence enables the truth to be present and to flow. This experience can also happen when listening to some musicians as in the National Concert Hall written about earlier.

All praise is judgement and must be delivered and received

carefully. It is positive and encouraging to receive affirmation, but that is not the reason for our work and no attachment should be on words of appreciation. Coming from the wrong source, like the voice of our cravings, words can be like a honeyed trap. One conscious breath enables us to understand our intention in giving praise and to discern the source and intent of people's words when we receive it. Taking this breath helps to keep us free. If we want to remain true to our path, there is never a time when we do not need our one conscious breath.

During our life we may take a series of flights. With each take-off we understand our ego, and with each landing we learn more about surrender and so arrive anew.

◯ Let's breathe

Breathing space	Breathing with Heart
Duration	Two minutes
Best for	Inspiring yourself and others
Outcome	To emanate positivity

Root your feet. Remember, this sends a clear signal to your mind that you are grounded and that you are going nowhere. Your body and the wisdom contained in it is going to be calling the shots for a little while. The thoughts in your head are purely a distraction.

The heart is where our love is and where our wisdom flows. The electromagnetic field of our heart is five hundred times stronger than our head. As you are still and spacious, you emanate love. Here you are filled with the heart's natural intelligence: love pulses and fear has no room. When we consciously breathe we are connected to our heart, and are home. We emanate love and there is no place for anything else.

This is where we are going in this short breath. It is a brief return to the energy we wish to be. It is a very powerful breath, and if you want to sustain it for longer, please go to the section on Coherent Breathing in the appendix (p267).

Take one conscious breath. Can you discern your mental state? If you are in ego, recognise it and smile. A smile expresses gratitude for your awareness. Now set the intention that with the next three breaths you are going to return to the centre of your heart, where your mind is stilled and from where your love flows.

Before you start, can you feel your heartbeat as you breathe? If so, we are going to coordinate breath and heart for six beats. Inhale for six heartbeats and exhale for the next six. Then repeat two more times. If this is not currently available, smile with this awareness and set the intention that it will be soon, and count for six seconds on each inhale and exhale.

Breathe, rest in being.

Chapter 22

Bandwidth and One Conscious Breath

Bandwidth is a psychological concept borrowed from computing and, before that, radio transmission.

In computing, it is the amount of data that is received every second, and is measured rather like the speed of water from a tap flowing into the bath. Our mind is the bath and just like it can only take so much information at a time. Whilst the bath physically overflows, our minds tend to overload and freeze. We become unable to process anymore and in the overwhelm cannot move forward.

Before universal laptops and smartphones, we had manually tuned radios. We turned a knob at the side of the radio to tune into a station. The more we could turn the knob and still have a clear signal indicated the bandwidth that the station broadcasted over. Bigger stations had more tolerance with more opportunity to tune into their signal. Bandwidth was the flexibility or width we had to tune in. This contrasts with the modern interpretation where it is purely the amount of data that is received and is independent of the mind's ability to process it.

The change in the use of bandwidth over just one generation reflects the added pressures put on our minds with the exponential rise in the opportunity for mental clutter as unfiltered data simply pours into us.

Some of the ways to cope with modern bandwidth overload include meditation, being kind to ourselves, and letting go of what is unnecessary. These are recurrent themes that are emerging in an exploration of one conscious breath. What if taking just one conscious breath helped us stay well and focused, particularly when we are online? It works for me. When I switch on my laptop, with this intention, I take just one conscious breath and as I work, I return to my breath as often as possible. To start, I used a timer to remind me every few minutes, but now it is routine. Try this as you are online and just check in with yourself after the breath to feel any differences in how you feel in your body.

Our bandwidth implies more data leads to more opportunities and is a good thing. With one conscious breath, we are more able to discern the value of the data and the impact it may have on our mental health. The breath acts as a valve enabling us to filter out and turn off from time to time. By taking just one conscious breath, we are breathing being, awareness and discernment into all this data, all this brain busyness. Isn't that a magnificent thought?

If we are exhausted from work, or if we are processing something huge in our life, our bandwidth will be maxed out. Everything else will happen more slowly because there is no headspace, no room for it. We live in this hyper-data-fed world – bringing a degree of consciousness and awareness to how we are in it has never been so necessary – yet with all the information available, it has never been so possible. Being and working healthily we become a role model, an agent for change. In a way, just by bringing our presence to the world at this moment in time we become modern-day contemplatives. We are all called to *be*.

The life of the contemplative has always been split between those who retreat from the world and those who are active in it. Whilst it has always been a harder route to stay conscious in the world with all its distractions and temptations, it is much harder still to stay conscious in today's hyper-data-fed world. All of us are called to tap into our inner contemplative.

Our attention is our greatest resource. (Please take note because when you do, everything changes.)

It is such an important concept, it needs time to be processed. Take a pause now and breathe this awareness. Reflect about how we take it for granted or overlook it. We literally overlook it and drain our power.

Oftentimes when we are online, we just give our attention away rent free to anything or anyone that comes our way. Have you heard the phrase 'to try to kill some time'? Please don't: remain conscious and aware of what you do. Don't burrow down endless rabbit holes online. Remember, your attention online is a resource, and the big tech companies want to monetise it. They are making money by renting your mind and your time out to advertisers (who are so much subtler and smarter than we can comprehend). It's like they have pasted a billboard advertising your attention somewhere you will never find it – inside your forehead. To be aware of this takes great self-discipline and mind vigilance.

More now than ever, we need people to be free, authentic and creative. To simply *be*. If not, tracts of society will be numbed out and zoned out, lost to an online addiction creating ignorance, and a lack of diversity and abundance. Like tracts of the Amazon rainforest, our minds will become deforested because we do not know of the precious roots of our attention.

We have never needed wisdom and authenticity as much as we do today. More facts will not save us, but more discernment and wisdom just might. By developing consciousness we can evolve to meet the needs of an uncertain future. As the pace of change accelerates, and the future becomes increasingly uncertain, we will need to bring ourselves along and cannot replicate the dysfunctional social and economic models that have been damaging our world for so long.

Be kind, take time and space and, where possible, breathe consciously. Unlike medication, there are no side effects or downsides to conscious breathing. When we are becoming maxed out, simply breathe. Breathe to discern, breathe to relax, breathe to be vigilant, and breathe to *be*. In the quiet of the rest after the breath, you will find something that is most truly you. By letting go at that point, you tune into authentic bandwidth – the universal no-thing. And in time, by letting go of that, by letting go of everything, you become everything – and everything becomes you. This is the source of the love that you are.

◯ Let's breathe

Breathing space	The Meeting Up With an Old Friend Breath
Duration	60 seconds
Response	To breathe among the overwhelm and chaos
Suited to	Parents, people who support people, and exhausted office workers
Outcome	Appreciation of what we can and can't do

When we feel overwhelmed, we naturally put our head in our hands, as if closing down our own mental computer system. Everything has become too much and we need to retreat from it all. Watch this tendency within yourself. If you get to this point, you may have missed a few conscious breaths along the way. Not to worry – let's use this awareness in this breath:

Put your head in your hands, one palm over each eye. Slowly take one conscious breath in this position. You will now take two more conscious breaths. With the exhale on each one, remove the palm of your hand from either eye. When you complete this, you open an awareness of overwhelm. You know that in getting to this point you have let things drift. It's like acknowledging to an old friend that you have both left it too long. But here your friend is the breath, and the occasion is just one conscious breath. Now smile at your friend and resolve that you will not leave it so long until you meet up again.

This breath is a breath of resolve. If ever a feeling of overwhelm persists and you are physically unable to cope with it, take immediate action. Try and get out into the fresh air and have a short walk, synchronising your breath with your steps.

Breathe slowly and consciously now. Rest in being.

Chapter 23

The Inclusive Breath

We are all unique expressions of source energy, of love.

Using Eknath Easwaran's example of the God seed, we are separate plants growing in one soil. Together we are one glorious flower bed of humanity. This flower bed contains all our diversity and notional nationality. We are simultaneously part of a large, unified world, and we are separate and unique.

Sometimes we overlook unity and just see separateness. Living in a foreign country for half my life, I have processed a sense of my own divergence and foreignness. As an Englishman living in Ireland, I knew it wasn't as straightforward as being English in England or Irish in Ireland. And over time my contrary nature kicked in. I started to identify as English in Ireland and Irish in England. When our boundaries are stretched by life, we open to the breadth and vulnerability of who we are. Here we see that the truth is much more colourful and diverse and it's the same for us all. I am. We are. It's just that.

The differences between us are literally skin deep. Yet when foreignness is spoken without embracing our own, we are separated into superficial groups of 'us' and 'them'. It's the same across the board. Working with a neurodiverse group of children for over twenty years, it became clear that their authenticity and vulnerability demanded mine. Viewing neurodiversity through the prism of the diversity within us, we begin to understand inclusion better, because once we understand that we are all diverse, we are unified by the acceptance of the heart.

When going on a school trip with our students, colleagues often felt exposed and removed from their comfort zone. Most of the time we were met with total acceptance within the community, but sometimes we'd encounter resistance. This often stemmed from a lack of exposure to the children's world. No school trip could ever be predetermined. Some neurodivergent children can get overwhelmed in certain environments and communicate this frustration behaviourally. Our staff were well-trained professionals and could deal with the occasional 'socially foreign' behavioural outbursts – but to the public eye the strategies used may have seemed unfamiliar and overly directive. We noticed most people wanted to support our situation, but although well-intentioned, public help could aggravate it. To alleviate the possibility for stress, we developed call cards for colleagues, to give to any members of the public, explaining the staff member's role and that further information was available via direct phone call. The cards created time and space. Time and space for the children to be supported appropriately in the community, and time and space for the public to deepen understanding.

When we view another person from a perspective of our own uniqueness, we see theirs and give them time and space to be. Divisions are of the ego. We create them because we are under the false assumption that we are separate. This is surface identity that wants us to identify with the mind and its contents and categorise everything.

But deeper down we see that all our divisions are made there. Whereas unity comes from our heart.

Although divisions are of the ego, as we deepen our understanding of it, we see the arbitrary nature of division. With awareness, we do not need to oppose; we see that the ego is not our enemy and that it has a benign role in our development. When the ego comes our way, we do not use it to create division – we acknowledge it gently with gratitude in a friendly way. Through kindness, we do not give it the reinforcement of opposing energy, and it quietly and gently recedes in significance. Remember – what we resist persists. In a way, we can take in the ego and adopt it with the same awareness we have in rehoming an energetic and endlessly distractable stray puppy. Maybe we can even give our ego a pet name, in the same way that my friend named his chimp earlier.

The ego has been written about a lot, and that's because once we truly understand this, everything changes. Arbitrary and artificial divisions fall away. Irish, English, American, Autistic – it's one and the same. From the perspective of our inner diversity, we see that our identity is not duality, nationality, personality, sexuality, individuality or 'whatsoeverality'. It is not one thing or another, it's 'both … and'. It is all the 'this' in 'that'. Once we start to identify with an 'ity', it's like we pull the curtains and add a blackout lining to them, so the light can't get in.

But when we open the curtains and wake up from ego, we wake to see that all our identities are all this now. I am now. We all are. We are held and contained by it. Together we are like a global raised flower bed, one wonderful spectrum of humanity in glorious array.

This spectrum of inclusion was embraced by the LGBTQ community in the 1970s with the adoption of the rainbow flag, and later by Desmond Tutu when he coined the phrase 'Rainbow Nation' as a symbol of hope and inclusion for post-apartheid South Africa. Both groups have known the depth of suffering from exclusion and prejudice. The rainbow has also been adopted as a symbol of neurodiversity as it emphasises the differences and unique strengths of neurodivergent people. The rainbow shows as a group we are diverse yet contained by one source. One rainbow – one spectrum – one love.

When we see it this way, it's impossible to have strong enemies, strong emotions, fixed positions because we start to see the truth in it all. The global spectrum of inclusion breathes the same air, and with every breath we have an opportunity to see all the 'this' in 'that'. As we wake up, we wake up to the present moment and all the diversity, abundance and foreignness within the now. Eventually our hearts and our homes get bigger; they transcend border crossings and our little cardboard passports. Our boundaries transform with greater inclusion and acceptance. From here, it is a short journey to know that our earth, our air, and nature are also who we are.

When we see the beauty in diversity, we embrace it and the wonderful lessons that flow our way. We can only do this once we have seen our own inner diversity and complexity and know that it's all okay. It can't be any other way; it's all okay because it's all from source. Any neurodiverse continuum is an expression of human wholeness and abundance, for we all are links of breath in the chain of humanity, and when we're conscious of this, we arrive at a place of inclusion and non-judgement.

From the depth and complexity within us we can embrace the depth and complexity of the other. We are fully united in the unlearning of it all when the no-thing in us sees the no-thing in the other and knows that we are all unique expressions of one consciousness. We become freer in our relationships – because when there is nothing to judge, there is nothing to hold onto. Across the spectrum of humanity, we all share this one true vocation, which is to be ourselves and to be in this world from here.

When we understand that we all breathe the same air and we are about to inhale what our neighbours have just exhaled, then how can we sustain any sense of separateness? Our breath becomes a silent thread of community and connection in the present moment. Simply through the air that we breathe, we experience each other.

Communities of breath and awakening are growing worldwide. I know because I am a member of one. By consciously breathing we get in touch with our being, and as we do so we exhale, which becomes a thread of being and connection with one another. Do you remember the game of pass the parcel in Chapter 5 where the parcel was unbundled to reveal the gift inside? It's a bit like that when we breathe together – except the gift is already unwrapped; it's our *Being*, and in breathing it we pass it to everyone in the room. This sharing of our breath becomes the thread of unity in community. But you don't need to be in a community of breath to experience this; you can just be on the bus. Breathe and be on the bus: let your calm and your breath do the talking.

◯ Let's breathe

Breathing space	The Inclusive Breath
Duration	60 seconds
Response	To bring a group together or hold space for a group
Suited to	Office employees and team managers
Best for	Team building
Outcome	Enhanced trust and creativity

Invite your team or your loved ones to take a collective conscious breath. Open your breathing circle by celebrating the diversity of the group, and spend two minutes appreciating each person present. At a deeper level still, know that there can be no division in a world where we all breathe the same air, and our energy flows from the same universal source.

Inhale.

Breathe, rest in being.

Chapter 24

Me and You Time

The foundation of community lies in our willingness to come together and be.

The children at school taught me a lot about community and what we called the 'me and you card' was a lovely way they would go about showing it. This all came about from our desire to reward them for doing their work.

From their perspective work have been when we asked something of them that they would rather not do. Come to think of it, isn't it just the same for the rest of us? It's work when its effortful, but it's not when it's not. Back to the children, to help overcome any resistance they were offered a small, suitable incentive. For some, this was a physical activity; time in the school garden; a small, preferred food item; time alone or watching something on a screen for a few minutes. These were called reinforcers. But, would you believe, there was a group of children, many of them teenagers, whose greatest reinforcement was 'me and you time'? Presented with an activity, they would hand over a card to show their choice. We may think that nonspeaking autistic students would be socially withdrawn and aversive of interaction at depth. But these same children are in fact expressing that nothing is as important as being with you. They are really saying, 'I just want to hang out and be with you. I want to share a laugh with you. You and me.' They are demonstrating that a deep connection has been made, and this is more valuable to them than anything else.

If only we 'neurotypicals' could be so direct and honest with our needs. Imagine how this would play out; we'd say something like, 'Look, I don't care about anything else right now, I just want to be with you. I don't care what we do. I just want to be here, with you, like now.' Just imagine what we can let go from this vantage point. Flowing in truth is the deepest connection we can make, and it avoids so many possibilities for misunderstandings and confusion.

Some children with autism have got this skill down pat. Many of them have a very strong emanation. And what they have naturally within, they sense in others. When they are with you, they are with you, and from this place, they know who is with them and who isn't. The being within them can be so strong that it recognises and draws out the being in others. When they see us in this way, they get us to up our game. These connections can be moments of pure joy. Like a magic trick, there is no 'me and you'. There is just 'us'. Us meeting in mutual being.

They have had to struggle so much with their divergence and how it is perceived on the outside, and they can be wounded by judgements. Yet they can emanate such a strong being. Being and being real they are so visibly authentic. The me and you card really says, 'I am. Are you? Can you be empty enough and authentic enough to be with me?' How about that as a foundation for community?

◯ Let's breathe

Breathing space	The One Love Breath
Duration	60 seconds
Response	To realise that we are all one
Suited to	Groups and communities
Best for	Gatherings and meeting
Outcome	Embracing one another in our diversity

One conscious breath is the skin between me and you, and it is the membrane between you and an awakening. Every conscious breath we take is a chance to wake up. Set an intention in your heart that when the time is right, you want to see things clearly.

Breathe, rest in being.

Chapter 25

The Frequency Holders

Eckhart Tolle calls people who embrace the rootedness of a group 'the frequency holders'.

Just by being themselves they quietly keep a group together and conscious. Due to the unassuming and unsung role they play, they often go unnoticed. Many of the school students were quietly, often unknowingly, doing their job. Being authentic and themselves was more than enough and much more than most of the rest of us. They had a role to keep us together and purposed. They were our frequency holders. Just by being themselves they were the guardians of the potential for the peace and joy of the school.

The L'Arche community understands this. L'Arche was initially established with the idea that the workers would commit to a life of community and would be at its centre, but as the model evolved, the workers came and went while the residents stayed put. It became clearer that the residents were the heart of the community. They were the passive actives – the frequency holders; holding fast to their authentic truth. They touched and transformed the lives of so many volunteers who came. The residents just were. They unobtrusively and undemonstratively welcomed and accepted the constant flow of volunteers who came with non-judgement and universal acceptance. This is L'Arche's welcome, which has touched and enhanced so many lives – mine included.

Community and organisational life is complex because of all the possibilities for different interactions from day to day. We're a bus ride full of egocentrics, leaders and frequency holders. In society, as the focus moves from the awakened individual to the collective, the chances are that the picture may become darker and more complex. Groups of people, unless consciously nurtured and with frequency holders, generally drift down towards unconsciousness. Large crowds are beset with complexity and often compounded by collective ego and unconsciousness, but add the right number of frequency holders to the mix and you will soon notice who is quietly leading who. The frequency holder does not take up space – they hold it; the frequency holder listens before speaking, and understands before seeking to be understood. The frequency holder does not pretend to know it all; they often stay put and quietly get on with stuff. Clearing the decks. Preparing the meals. They are like the egg holding society's cake mix together.

In the Tao, wisdom grows in uncertainty: this is the path of unlearning or not knowing. A mind that does not know the answers contains infinite potential because it is present in the field of possibilities. The same applies to the Frequency Breath. This is a breath that holds the room by mere consciousness of its flow, and weighted presence. Like the unknowing mind, The Frequency Breath is open, inclusive and curious. Like the feeling of peace and possibility that flows from an acknowledgement that 'I don't know', this quiet, unassuming breath keeps its cool and gently starts to guide us, which is why we look for it more and more in difficult situations.

As we bring our conscious breathing with us to every aspect of our life, let us use the Frequency Breath to quietly hold space, embrace the uncertainty and build connection. In a room full of talking heads, things may appear chaotic, but events can be touched by a quiet, unassuming listening breath.

Full disclosure: If you have the role to be a frequency holder, like so many of the children at our school, thank you – society owes you one.

◯ Let's breathe

Breathing space	The Frequency Breath
Duration	60 seconds
Response	An appreciation of all group roles, especially underappreciated ones
Suited to	Group members, particularly those who are recognised as having responsibility
Best for	Affirmative team building
Outcome	Appeciation of the underdog

In your mind's eye, see a team you work with. Ideally one you have responsibility for. I want you to notice the unnoticed ones. The quiet ones. The ones who don't get many of the accolades or bonuses or compliments. In society these people often carry what is perceived on the outside as a disadvantage and falsely get recognised for this rather than the energy of peace and reconciliation that they bring. Can you make a list of them?

Take them one by one. Say their name and then consciously breathe for one minute. But before you do, ask your unconscious a question. Set an intention that by the end of the breath you are going to see them and appreciate them afresh. Once you start to appreciate them, the energy changes, and the floodgates will open. In the quietness of their being often lies a loyal, steadfast and loving heart. When you become coherent and open your heart, you will see theirs much more clearly.

Breathe, rest in being.

Chapter 26

The Camino Breath

A Camino is a pilgrim path. We set off with our destination in mind and slowly, step by step, we get there, sometimes before we realise it.

It is like life in microcosm. In a sense, life is a pilgrim path and the steps we make are the breaths we take. Somewhere along the path of conscious breathing we realise we have arrived. Our destination is not where we set out for but simply to be here now, on the way now, breathing now.

I recently completed my first Camino in Portugal and Spain. I started walking just above Lisbon and continued up the way to Santiago. I had just finished my work at the school and it was a one-month transition from one phase of life to another. The simple rhythm of it became my life. Walk, eat, sleep. Repeat. For twenty-eight days. In the simplicity of it, it was as if I shed layers of complexity and resistance that I had built up at work all these years. The simple repetition became the norm, and it softened my old work shell.

Since this was my first Camino, I spent a couple of days at Tomar, north of Lisbon, to find my bearings. I was unsure about the navigation so decided to amble out to the start to find the way before setting off properly the next day. Prior to entering an overgrown forest, a fingerpost pointed two ways. One seemed to be indicating a wet weather route through the side roads, and the other a dry weather one along a river valley and through a huge eucalyptus forest. I opted for the dry route. It soon became apparent that this was very much the unmarked way and the path less travelled. I was alone, 500 kilometres from Santiago in the middle of a forest in the middle of Portugal, and soon became comprehensively lost. I decided to retrace my steps but got further entangled in the wood. Being unprepared and not expecting any drama on a rest day, I had left my map and phone behind. The options to get out were narrowing. I went old school and listened out for the sound of a road. With the silence of the forest, my concern grew. I was frightened. Although I was doing everything I could with my breath to regulate the panic, panic had the upper hand. Dusk was falling. Eventually I heard an isolated road and after a few more kilometres came to a signpost. Tomar was just seven kilometres away. I just had to follow the signs. After an early scare I wised up. I resolved to always have both my map and phone and soon learned to locate the telltale signs for pilgrims among the trees and rocks of the forest. With this experience so soon under my belt, I was able to find my way to Santiago without further drama.

When I got back to my pension though, I realised that in the loss and panic of the afternoon, the greatest thing I had lost was my senses. I put my head in my hands. Even though I tried to come back to my senses with rounds of Box Breathing at the time (p269), this was like trying to regulate a fire that I had let get out of control. To really learn from this episode, I needed to retrace my breaths and my steps to a much earlier point in time before the fire and before I was lost. Then it hit me: this was *my* Camino and it needed to be walked *my* way. Everything including my breath had to be in step, and I had to be open to where that might lead me.

Where it led me was someplace wonderful. I understood that this was a way of the heart. A way of connection with people. This surprised me as my default mode is somewhat solitary and introverted – my life up to then had probably been a little more the observer than a participant. But during the Camino, I was open and available to what came my way. As people opened to me, my way opened. I enjoyed the companionship of strangers. Being present to one another on the way and then parting, sometimes to meet again, sometimes not. It didn't much matter what came next – the key was to consciously breathe and to walk with a free and open heart.

In travelling light, everything unnecessary was shed. This was a simple way of heart and breath, and everything came into focus. This is the central message of all the world religions I had studied for so many years. Heart and breath. This wonderful simplicity was *my* way and through the Camino it became embodied.

I didn't want my Camino to end – but I had reached Finisterre (Fin De Terra) and had literally run out of road. But there is great hope in completion. Like many pilgrims do, I understood that my Camino only started in Santiago and my job was to bring it home. In sharing it and breathing it I return to it, even in the depths of the darkness of a Dublin winter.

Whether your Camino is a destination, a moment of crisis and resolve, a period of lost and found, or simply just the steps on the way, it is *your* way. Don't judge it. Just walk it. Be grateful for it opening and revealing itself to you – whatever it looks like. In undertaking it with heart and breath, you may in fact find that you've already arrived.

◯ Let's breathe

Breathing reflection

As you continue with your own Camino of taking just one conscious breath, your Way will open. The spirit of breath is open and inclusive in this way. What you see may become a bit more complex. But it will be authentic and it will be you, going your way.

Breathe, rest in being.

Chapter 27

Look Who's Talking

As we awaken, we realise that the desire to give advice tends to come from ego.

There is sometimes a need to demonstrate just how right and wise we really are. This desire to be 'seen' as wise can also signal the development of a spiritual ego. It is a sign that our ego has not given up the game; it has transmuted into something smarter and wised up. Don't trust it.

Growing up, 'look who's talking' was a phrase I heard and probably used a lot. It is an ego-based statement of comparison. You're telling me to do this or do that, but 'just look who's talking' – you're not doing it in any case. In other words, you're not telling me the truth because you're not living it. The interaction would often be rounded off with something like, 'You're no great shakes yourself.' This language seems dated now, but what we have here is a clash of egos, entrenching one another in ego positions.

On one level the response is correct – do not preach to me until you are fully on message. Yet we are never fully on our message until it flows from being, from our heart. Ironically, when people are in being, they are much less likely to give advice or make comparative statements – or write books!

'Look who's talking' becomes a negative feedback loop. Like with like. Positivity leads to positivity, but negativity leads to negativity. These are two different energy cycles which describe chains of events that have negative and positive responses. They are *vicious* and *virtuous* cycles. In a vicious cycle, ego is met with more ego, and its retrenchment follows with the interaction spiralling down. Whereas in a virtuous cycle, being inspires being, which points to the truth.

The need to be seen as smart is the potential banana skin for every self-proclaimed guru (and author). The question we must ask at this point is, what is this need? If it is to spread understanding and learning, irrespective of its outcome, then it is a good thing. But if it is to demonstrate our cleverness or our wisdom, it may well be that the ego has discarded this banana skin on our path.

The modern world which has us always on, unless punctuated by conscious breaths or a woken mind, frequently puts the whole body and nervous system on edge. When our always-on society meets dysfunctional collective and individual egos, there is a danger of generating toxic organisations and toxic bodies. A survey of 120,000 respondents over 122 countries revealed that more people experienced negative feelings and anxiety in 2021 than ever before.[23]

Our minds can't distinguish between an external threat and a thought. A mind-made thought, often ego jibber-jabber, is perceived as having the same status and threat as something outside and real. It is extremely significant when we understand our worries are interpreted and responded to in the same way as something that really puts us in danger. Busy, restless minds create busy, restless bodies. Whereas relaxed attentive minds lead to relaxed bodies.

It is important to know that our false selves, our egos, have skin in the game, and do not want to be found out. Just like the spiritual ego, they will wise up and mutate. As we awaken, our egos take subtler and subtler iterations to avoid detection. Worse still, as has already been said, they may even try to unconsciously sabotage our progress and start to discard banana skins on the path.

Seeing is freeing: as you start to uncover the truth, the need to be right dissolves, the ego becomes more fully revealed and we start to understand just who has been talking to us all along. Think about that for a minute. When you are in the company of someone whose consciousness is evolving, ask questions that enable them to find their own truth. Here you give space and act like a mirror that reflects their own truth back to them. People who have a very strong emanation can also do this in silence, rather like some of the children at school did for me.

So, how do we breathe through the ego?

An awakened mind is examined and understood and from this space will finally give our bodies the opportunity to rest, which is what they have been crying out for. When we start to awaken the gap between our thoughts and our bodies, response opens. Our body has time to hear the truth. It literally gives us a chance to understand 'just who is talking', to respond with awareness and stop habitual reactions to what is unnecessary.

The settled mind finally communicates the clear glass of water. The path from awareness to contentment opens. From here the body relaxes and starts to feel what truth feels like on the inside. And it feels good.

The holy grail of relaxed attention is in sight, as is the ultimate virtuous cycle. The wheel has stopped spinning and has been replaced with a virtuous circle of being–relaxation–being–relaxation. The body and mind are in sync, and supportive of one another. Once the body knows who is talking, it starts to know the truth and wants more of it.

Slowly, a virtuous circle of peace and joy being met with relaxation and ease, and leading to more peace and joy, becomes established. With ego cravings aside, positive momentum builds, and we are on the pathway of wholeness and integration.

◯ Let's breathe

Breathing space	The Intention and Attention Breath
Duration	60 seconds
Response	To listen deeply to ourselves
Best for	Fresh starts and clarity seeking
Outcome	Getting in touch with inner guidance

Where do you really want to put your attention? Take one conscious breath. *Inhale for three seconds.*

Your attention is probably your most precious of resources, and your most overlooked. *Exhale for six seconds.*

We know of the jibber-jabber and the cluttered mind, and we know that peace is not found there. But if we try and keep them at bay, we will reinforce it. Remember, what we resist persists. We want to listen to who is really talking, which is our quiet voice – the voice that shows us the way. Breath workers call this inner guidance. *Inhale for three seconds.*

Have trust that with one conscious breath we change the mind's dynamic and momentarily erase some of the statements on our mental screen. We are not that. We were never that. It is just clutter. *Exhale for six seconds.*

When we erase clutter, we create the awareness and conditions to discern the way forward. The voice of guidance is often heard in silence; we have to be attentive to the whole field of possibilities.

Breathe, rest in being.

Chapter 28

Spacious Listening

Breathing builds generous listening.

Reflective practices where we listen to the quiet within ourselves and watch our thoughts internally help us to develop our capacity for deep, self-knowledge. These practices include meditation, reflective prayer, yoga, tai chi and breathwork among many. Attentively listening to ourselves in this way is a natural step to attentively listening to someone else. Just one conscious breath is a great way to listen to ourselves. The moment we press the pause button and understand that this pause is more about who we are than what we are thinking, we awaken awareness.

I am always struck by the incredible amount of listening my general practitioner does. He never knows what is coming through the door yet in ten minutes or so must listen, record, examine and discern the truth. Despite this, some doctors seem to give you a sense that they have all the time in the world. I appreciate it when there is an interval between patients – my GP told me he practises mini-mindfulness sessions between them. I know he is listening because he is fully available, there is no clutter from his last patient or worry about future ones – he is with me now. This is the heart of the consultation. His inner state as a listener inspires me, and I always come out feeling lighter, irrespective of the outcome.

Attentive listening is reflective and is the wisdom gap of the communication process. When we listen to another person fully, we turn off our judging mind and free up the possibility to respond rather than react. Taking a conscious breath as we listen keeps the listening focused and on track, and when we listen deeply, everything changes. Everything is revealed to us when we are leaned in, ready and open – and free to receive what comes.

Epictetus, a Greek philosopher, is attributed with the saying that we have two ears and one mouth, so we can listen twice as much as we speak. Listening is far more important than talking and is the key in the conversational dyad because when the listener is in being, it inspires the speaker to up their game. When we sit in conversation with another person, we can make the choice to operate from our being or from our ego, and so can they. In this way there are four different interactional dyads at play: 1. being–being; 2. being–ego; 3. ego–being; and 4. ego–ego. The last of the four, ego–ego, is our human default. This is still the main dyad we see in human exchanges and is the basis of probably nine out of ten interactions. Being–being, which may be around one or two in a hundred, is where transformation can take place. This is compassionate listening that the Tao says is key to transforming the world.

When we speak and listen from the heart, free of ego, we find the way. This is how we tap into our Listening Breath. Being–being is the point of unity. It is where we arrive at the same place together, free of ego on either side; it is here we feel truly heard and in our heart space. When you are awake to being–being, you will find yourself listening more and talking less. We listen most deeply when the inner stillness in us hears the inner stillness in another. The truth of any interaction is known by our bodies. If we go away from an interaction with another person feeling lighter and affirmed, we have encountered being, but if we feel drained, we have met ego. Imagine the transformational nature that our meetings would have if we each set the intention that at the end of the conversation, we wanted our companion to feel lighter.

Listening to teenagers

I often struggled with the complexities of parenting, particularly in the teenage years. I know the many layers family relations come with because I have done more than my share of creating confusion. Family life provides lessons when we are at our most fraught, frayed and vulnerable. This can especially be the case when listening to teenagers. Here, communication can be quite infrequent, and we are almost grateful when it comes around, whatever the context.

I have been guilty of waiting for the gap and using it as my chance to talk, defend, justify or question. It's like the gap is the only opportunity to get my piece in, as an adult, so I feel that I must take it. I prey on it, in fact. But when we fill the gap in this way, our teenagers do not walk away feeling heard. What we say will be counterproductive and will go on to exacerbate the core problem. Here, more than in most conversational dyads, we need to mind the gap and enjoy the space that arises and see what flows from it. Patience precedes the Listening Breath. Very few teenagers ever say they wish their parents gave them more advice, but many of them will say that they wish they felt more heard.

As parents, we need to be aware of our ego status. When the listener is in ego, there really is no hope of an interaction of any value or depth. Like attracts like, so ego in us will provoke ego elsewhere. Ego is present when our being is absent – simply inhabiting our heart creates our being. Picture the smile of the neurodivergent pupil – there you have it. Remember all the mind-identified states: fear, anxiety, disillusion and anger are all ego-based states. Showing up as we are for our teens, and not where we *need* to be, or how 'right' we need to be, opens the possibility for greater honesty.

Compassionate listening is the highest goal of conversation. It is a quiet attentive state, that uses breath as its bedrock. We show just how well we are listening when we breathe through our noses. Gently, focused, present. In addition to helping the mind of the listener settle, breathing this way portrays a sense of containment and waiting. We are still and open, yet our mouth is shut. The talker sees this and realises on an unconscious level that we are there for them and we are not about to jump in or butt in with our 'but'. They intuitively understand we have time; we are present, and the space that they need to be heard is within us. This encourages the talker to express themselves fully and openly.

When the listener is in being, they can discern where the speaker is coming from. We are only available to listen to another when we have experienced it first hand ourselves and know what it feels like. Our breath helps us to discern when we are in an ego state. When we wake up to our ego it is like there's a fork in the road. The path we must tread is invariably the other one in the other direction. It's like we've come across a sign – 'Unstable conditions ahead. Path closed.' – and we simply must head back. When the speaker senses the 'head-back' from the listener, they are given nonverbal permission to head back themselves, and so can converse from their best selves.

Listening is a beautiful thing. It's transformative, in the easiest way. Listening from the heart is probably the most important thing we ever do for our relationships. Every true relationship, and every true conversation, starts with spacious listening.

To start to listen, to really listen to others, listen to yourself and understand where you are coming from. Remember to breathe through your nose as you listen. Prior to meeting someone, or before a telephone conversation, set an intention that through the power of your listening you want them to feel lighter. You want to ease a situation just with the power of your listening. This does not mean you take someone's burdens on your shoulder. But rather, you create inner spaciousness with your breath that gives room to be and to be heard.

We ready ourselves for listening by being empty of our stuff. Without any internal distractions, we can be more present to another person and their stuff. We do not take it on. When we are contained in our own breath, we are going nowhere, we are present, so we can hold their stuff and help them to let go. This is the start of the process of transformational listening.

I have discovered the very deepest questions are answered when we don't ask them at all. A question can sometimes act as a breath blocker and stop flow. It can be felt as an intrusion and create resistance. Instead, ask nothing. Just wait, open the space in the spirit of non-judgement, and be. Breathe through the nose. *Wait, wait*. And there, there it is.

◯ Let's breathe

Breathing space	The Listening Nasal Breath
Duration	60 seconds
Response	To return to presence; be open and listen from this place
Suited to	Conversation partners
Best for	Parent–teenager conversations; parent–child conversations; job interviews' online meetings
Outcome	Centring; waiting and responding from essence

Our breath acts as the signpost. How we are feeling is revealed by how we are breathing. Befriend your breath and check in with it as often as possible by taking one conscious breath. Remember, we signify an active state of listening and containment to our partner by breathing through the nose. They know that we are listening because we are not waiting for an opportunity to say something. *Pause. Be still.* Breathe consciously through your nose as you listen as often as you can.

Practise a nose breath. Hold still. Settle the mind. Pretend you are alone in the universe, and all you can see is the tip of your nose. See the fresh air gently flowing in and flowing out. Do not force this – just relax and let it be. This is the Listening Breath. It needs no grand entrance. Let it greet you. Just you, your nasal passage, and the person in front of you. Inhale through the nose. Exhale through the nose.

Listen. By nose breathing, you send reassuring signals to people you meet, and to your body. You're saying, it's okay – I am here, and I hear. Whether they see it or not at a conscious level, they will register it unconsciously. The work is being done. This reassures them and gets them to open more. The more we breathe through our noses when in conversation, the deeper the process of transformational listening becomes.

When you consciously breathe, especially through your nose, not only are you more contained but you communicate it too. Undertake an experiment: Watch people who are nose breathing as they listen. How is the conversation flowing? Can you compare this with dyads when people are mouth-breathing?

Breathe, rest in being.

Chapter 29

Developing Rapport

Rapport happens when two people or a small group are in sync.

It can also be seen when a performer is able to read the room and begins to understand their audience. In the first chapter it happened when the jazz singer was scat singing. Sometimes it is helpful to be on the outside looking in; visualise that you are watching a TV chat show when the host and the guest reach a point of flow and the interview seems to take on a life of its own.

In Ireland, which has been my home for the last thirty years, chat and chat shows are almost an art form. Here *The Late Late Show* is an institution and has been going for more than sixty years. It is the world's longest-running chat show. Chat flows more naturally here than in England where I was born. In England, it sometimes feels that we talk more from our head and conversation is punctuated with more facts. In Ireland, the flow of conversation is often freer, more from within, a little less predictable, and more left field.

Over the years I have seen some interviews on *The Late Late Show* where the host and guest seem to be in flow. But how did they get there? It takes a very confident host to actively listen to the guests and not have their next question prepared. When the time is right, the interviewer will interject with a question, or even better, a breath sound such as *hmm*. This says, 'I'm here; I hear you and am letting things go with the flow.' What better sign of rapport could there be than to hear that? *Hmm*.

So as the interview unfolds, a deeper truth emerges. The being of the host is present to the being of the guest and vice versa. The depth of the interview goes way beyond the words being said. If you observe the breath of both people at this time, it flows freely and smoothly and is often in sync.

Some people have such a strong emanation that they can short-circuit all this and inspire people silently just with their being. Great spiritual teachers can do this without saying a word – just like many of our pupils did for me. Their presence inspires presence within those they meet. One of the Buddha's greatest sermons was a silent transmission when he held up a white lotus flower, for followers to know of the 'jewel' at its centre. This jewel is like knowing the smile of a nonspeaking neurodivergent child.

The lotus flower is very significant in Buddhism as it is associated with awakening; it is a potent symbol that something so pure and so perfectly white can silently emerge every morning from the depths of pond sludge. One disciple became immediately enlightened. This sermon became the source for the direct transmission that subsequently evolved into Zen Buddhism.

This use of silence is also used in psychotherapy. The Rogerian tradition uses the space in the therapist to support the space in the client and they say very little as a result. The shared space held primarily by the therapist empowers the client to sort it out for themselves. Breathwork with a qualified and experienced breath worker is similar: the breath worker leads the client so the client can embody their truth and find their own answers within. Talk therapy works on the outside in, whereas breathwork works from the inside out. In both methods, the therapist is trained to hold space securely and safely for another person. When a breath worker does this, they dedicate time to exploring the key issues that need resolution, and ask the client to set an intention for the session. After leading their client into the breath, they get themselves out of the way and let the breath get on with the work of inner transformation.

Let's picture again the transformational nature of the smiles of the children at work. At these times the children have such a strong presence they just *are*, and they radiate being and essence in these moments. Nothing gets in the way of this direct transmission, and people who are attuned to it can very quickly reach a point of rapport with them. Being with these children is not straightforward, but if we are open, they open us to our clutter and inner stuff. Some of their presence is so strong that they act as a mirror to awareness.

When we become emptier, we have the time and space to be. In that time and space, we understand the need for time and space in the other, and as this is reciprocated it becomes a naturally reinforcing conversation. With the interaction of silent being to silent being, a virtuous cycle of reinforcement develops.

This isn't just for a breathwork session; it can be successfully practised during a work meeting. Take just one silent conscious breath, and watch how you feel. The more you do, the more you will be able to emanate positivity and create rapport with another person. Remember, the pace of your breath is key. Coherent Breathing is explored in the appendix (p267); the optimal breath rate for this is between four and six breaths a minute.

◯ Let's breathe

Breathing space	The Rapport Breath
Duration	10 minutes, off and on
Response	To align yourself with your partner to create flow
Outcome	Revived spirit; reconnecting with 'I am'

Your objective here is to get the most creative juice out of a meeting. You will not do this by opposing one another but rather by getting in joint flow. You do not have to say you are doing this if you feel it would be received as 'woo-woo'.

What I suggest is that you listen to the gaps in the conversation and breathe into them. Don't respond until you yourself have taken a conscious breath. Slow it all down and attend to the gaps in the language as much as the content. Now try and model your breath for your companion. Start by mirroring their breath and make audible breath onomatopoeias. Remember we encountered them in Chapter One. They are the sighs and *wows* and *hmms* that naturally punctuate our conversations. Use them, especially *hmm*. You are now modelling and influencing flow, and creating the best conditions for an open and creative conversation. You are much less likely to recycle old hurts and dynamics in this way and much more likely to break fresh ground.

Breathe, rest in being.

Chapter 30
Pace

Listening and pace are very closely linked because when something is spoken or said with the right pace, the listener can understand it much more deeply.

When we are delivering something and talking from being, it can sound as if we are talking from one space to another. Here the space, rather than the words, guides the communication. Think of a frog crossing a pond crested with lily pads. The leaps are what get it to the other side. But the jumps are enabled by the pause and the rest of the lily pad. Without the lily pads, the journey cannot be made. It is the same with speaking from being – without the pause, it is not possible.

In 1981 I went Interrailing with a friend. We crossed from Southeast England to France, Spain, and then from the Spanish border on a slow rackety overnight train into Porto from the north. As we travelled, we moved from the known and the familiar to the unknown and unfamiliar. But soon after we pulled into Sao Bento station in Porto just after dawn, we moved from the unfamiliar to complete shock. It was market day and all the farmers had come in from the adjacent lands of the Douro Valley and beyond. Watermelons were piled securely yet unfathomably high on old worn wooden carts pulled by water buffaloes with long polished horns. I had never seen a watermelon or a water buffalo before. Then I looked in the café windows and saw farm workers who had been up before dawn getting everything ready for market, drinking shots from bottles stuffed with pickled lizards and other unknown reptiles. Two teenagers coming from the shelter of Southeast England, and travelling for three days and nights by train, we were shunted into a wonderful state of complete chaos and unfamiliarity. It was such a gloriously alien world that we literally could have pulled into Timbuktu Central Station on the overnight train. This was my first real travel experience; it took my conceptual lid off, and I will always love Porto for that.

I had returned for the first time. The gap between my two visits was forty years and, in that period, it was as if Porto too had come of age. European Union membership and inclusion had brought this magical city on the very edge of Europe into something even more. There were new art galleries, an internationally acclaimed modern art campus, a world-class music centre designed by a renowned architect, a bookshop which was the inspiration for the Hogwarts library in the Harry Potter books, great contemporary restaurants, and for a European city with a strong history of the past and empire, the vibe and the feeling in Porto was one of modernity and becoming.

We had a tour of one of the UNESCO-protected port houses on the banks of the Douro River. The port is made in the Douro Valley and is sent downstream to be aged and cellared in the warehouses. Our tour was wonderful. The guide intuitively knew the sweet spot of pace at which to deliver her commentary and guided us not from the words but from their absence. During a tour delivered from a script and repeated many times a day, the pace of delivery was the main way that she could convey essence. Because she was unrushed and paced her delivery intuitively, we were able to be present in her presence. The gaps in her delivery enabled the being of our guide to communicate at a much deeper level and resonated with our internal space.

Pace and space are a central part of how we communicate. It is the punctuation of our speech, and it is here that we communicate from being. In talking about pace and space I am essentially talking about nothing, so perhaps it is easier to read of some examples:

Reflect now on sitting in the company of someone who talks very quickly. It's an impressive sign that they can keep up with their own motor running so fast. It's a sign that their thoughts are racing. But for the listener, it is tiring to process. We are waiting for the gap to open in all the words. Without this gap, there is no space for the talker to pause and be, and there's no space for the listener to hear deeply and process. Listening to a fast talker is rather like watching the old black and white movies with the prairie trains rattling through the Midwest. Everything goes by in a whirr and a cloud of dust, and it's impossible to see the carriages and how everything is held together.

Pace also happens in sports when we listen to our bodies. Over the last few years, I had the privilege of being a member of a local running group with wonderful and committed coaching for adults. This combined with the support of a very positive group found me on the start line of the Dublin City Marathon, a more unlikely place could not have been predicted a few years earlier. I was terrified. Would my body stand it? How would I ensure I had enough energy to get around? What if I hit the wall and 'blew up?' What if? What if? My head and my fears were in overdrive. We were well coached and told to start slow, as slow as we dared, and not get caught up in the pace and the energy of the run; to watch ourselves as a runner and to listen to our inner voice. If it all got overwhelming, we were advised to just rest behind someone who was running in a club jersey as they would also be coached and following a plan. To run a marathon we need discipline to train over many months, the right pace, to be watchful of ourselves and our motives, to focus on the inner rather than the outer, and we need a mentor. It's not difficult to see how people liken running a marathon to a form of spiritual practice.

In particular, the importance of pace can be seen when working with neurodivergent children. One of the things we said to all new staff at the start of the year was, this is a marathon and not a sprint. New staff, in particular, could get overtaken with positivity, rather like the energy of the early stages of a marathon, and dive in head first. The danger was that this is the route to burnout. To get all staff and children safely to the end of the year, careful pacing was required. Conversely, colleagues who really got the best out of working with children with autism and complex needs intuitively understood the need for pace and space.

In the past when we visited someone, we would ring the doorbell and wait. Nowadays we are more likely to send a text to say we are outside. We all know that the sensitive thing to do is to ring and wait patiently. It is the very same when working with neurodivergent children. We need to understand that some children might take their time to respond to their name. This can be up to fifteen seconds and is simply the time between pressing their bell and getting a response, and like all sensitive guests, we must press once and wait attentively and kindly. The key is to make the request such as, 'Brad walk with me,' and wait, mind the gap for up to fifteen seconds, and be present to the response, however it arrives. The interaction goes: request–smile–be and wait in kindness, like an extended conscious breath. Wait here, free of judgement and all jibber-jabber, and free of the expectation that things will go the way they are in your head.

Standing on the outside waiting, fifteen seconds can feel an agonisingly long time, and the temptation comes to fill the gap with yet more requests – more clutter. So, it could go, 'Brad, Brad, Brad, Brad, Brad...' in an increasing tone of frustration. But what Brad may be experiencing is that someone very impatient and rude is outside, continually ringing his buzzer and giving him no head space. All he is doing is taking the time he needs to respond but is being further bombarded with escalated requests and clutter. *Buzz, buzz, buzz, buzz, buzz.*

This pattern gets repeated over and over, and Brad becomes averse to the sound of his name, so when someone says, 'Brad, Brad,' he no longer hears his name; what he hears is, 'Here we go again,' and so this understandably acts as a trigger for him. When we are open to learning from neurodivergent students directly in this way, we are taught awareness through direct transmission. Like the smack of awakening from a Zen master. *Smack.*

Communicating between partners can follow the same pathway. If one person feels they haven't been heard, they may repeat the question several times. But, if the listener feels they are being bombarded or nagged, they might just shut down and a vicious communication cycle develops. The key is to listen when we listen. Pace the speaker. Demonstrate how you are doing this by listening through eye contact, nasal breathing, nodding, and the like. Also slow them down by responding deliberately and attending to the space between your words. Model what you want to hear and give them the opportunity to hear in the silence in the gaps. But if you can't listen and be fully available, just say so. Oddly, one of the most reassuring signs that we are being heard is when the listener says they weren't listening and asks their partner to repeat what they said.

○ Let's breathe

Breathing space	The Pause Breath
Duration	10 minutes or so during a meeting
Response	To model calm and flow
Best for	Heated exchanges
Outcome	Turning down the dial; avoiding hazards

Remember the example of the frog crossing the pond crested with lily pads? The pads enabled the crossing by giving moments to pause safely and go again. It's the same in a meeting, especially a heated one.

The key whenever something is too hot is to dial it down. We do this by slowing it down. Slowing our delivery and generating gaps with the breath. This also gives us time to become coherent so what we say is what we want to say rather than what our reflexes are shouting at us. Our conscious breath makes us intentional and responsive. It's like we have a ship's mate on the upper deck providing safe passage, throttling back on the engines and giving time to spot where the icebergs are. Always try and be attentive to the space and pace in how you are communicating. Give yourself space now. Take just one fully conscious breath.

Breathe, rest in being.

Part 3

Smile

The evolution of just one conscious breath is deepening and evolving with writing.

First it was to breathe and to rest in the stillness and spaciousness after the breath. As awareness grows, a smile of gratitude is added. Have the picture of the heart smile of the nonspeaking neurodivergent pupil as your inspiration. So smile as you let go, grateful that your ego is no longer blocking your path.

When we let go of something as important as our awareness and understanding, we trust deeply. The breath of letting go is a sigh. When we hear it, smile because we are starting to hear the wisdom of surrender. Read the following chapters with a smile of gratitude for your growing awareness of knowing of your ego, and sigh as you let go into the endless possibilities of deep surrender.

Breathe. Rest in being. Smile. And sigh.

Chapter 31
Breathing Gratitude

'Accept what is in front of you without wanting the situation to be other than it is.'

– The Tao De Ching

Rest in being is how we begin Part Three of this breathing journey.

It is how I close off a breathing session and is an acceptance of the here and now. It is self-love. It is the Way. To rest in being feels like a shoulder drop, a sigh, a long generous exhale into the universe. This is what I wish for you – and this is what you should wish for you too. But how do we get there, and how do we sustain it? We begin with one word: gratitude.

As we struggle, we create resistance. This blocks the even flow of breath, which then restricts our energy. It interrupts the flow from source, which reduces the life force in our life. You can visualise resisting and interrupting this flow of energy from source as prematurely ending a hug with someone then self-consciously patting them on the back.

Accepting what we know and what we have, free of judgement, is how we begin our path towards gratitude and joy. This is the state of self-contentment and acceptance of life as we know it, and it's a mental liberation we are always in search of. Resting in being arrives without judgement, interference, or status. It is and it flows from what is; acceptance of this creates alignment.

Gratitude is not something we need to express to someone – we can quietly model and emanate it. It supports us, because when we are grateful, we are open and positive to everything around us and this helps create the conditions for our God seed to grow. Over time this practice of gratitude deepens and becomes a way of living more positively. Gratitude helps us to accept the present moment for what it is and to be with the peace of simply being. From a place of gratitude, it is time to add a smile to the practice of one conscious breath after the period of stillness that follows the exhale. This is the smile of gratitude inspired by the children at school and the life and work of Thich Nhat Hanh, written about in the next chapter.

Some of the children I worked with found waiting difficult. We all do, but it could be overwhelming for them. So we introduced opportunities for them to wait in their day. This could be really hard, but staff remained present and, when the time was up, showed their gratitude to the children. Over time and reinforcement, the children learned to wait for gratitude. Similarly, when we are grateful, we can delay gratification and accept what comes as it comes. In gratitude we care less about what happens next as we are content here now.

Back in the introduction, we discovered that the word 'inspire' comes from the Latin phrase 'to breathe in'. By taking a fully conscious breath in gratitude, your breath becomes your source of inspiration. As you consciously breathe, you open internal space, known as our wisdom gap. Internal space gives time to reflect and make the transition from reaction to response. Rather like sleeping on your response, your breath opens a gap between your thoughts and provides the space for the response to be touched with internal wisdom. Imagine the possibilities! Consciously breathing prior to offering up a response is even more powerful than sleeping on it – because when we breathe, we are awake. We are conscious.

Let's take a pause in the middle of this chapter. Explore a grateful conscious breath as it enters, filling you up with life. Bring it down deeper into your body. Low and slow. Pause very slightly. Slowly exhale and feel the tingle of air as it leaves your body. Rest in the stillness that follows that glorious exhale of it all. Be here now. And smile. Smile in gratitude.

Practise this as often as you can. Try not to respond to anything or say something until you take one fully grateful conscious breath with a smile. Your actions will come from within and will be touched with the wisdom of not immediately knowing. If we respond purely at a head level, then this is mental stuff and has our ego at its source. Egos need to be right. They need to demonstrate just how right they really are and will take on all comers to prove their point and demonstrate how clever they are. God knows I have been clever and right so many times in this way. We all have. We will all continue to be. But as we watch our breath and introduce a wisdom gap, we become more reflective and self-aware. We also make that hugely significant karmic shift from reacting (ego-based mental stuff) to responding within from a place of love. We make that profound shift from our head to our heart, first written about in the letter at the beginning of the book.

Take this conscious breath in gratitude as often as you can, particularly before any points of transition or exchange with another person. Watch your thoughts as they deepen as you become aligned with this breath. Repeat this practice whenever you can. Slowly the curtains that have been drawn across your reality will reveal the truth. Your inner truth begins to align with the outer truth. Have no expectations of this process, just accept. Expectations cast our minds to the future and away from life and the breath. Breath is now. You cannot multitask with conscious breathing. You can only consciously breathe in the present moment. With this breath, you are now. Here there is nothing between you and life and so you become one with its flow.

◯ Let's breathe

Breathing space	Breath of Gratitude
Duration	30 seconds
Response	To fully accept being here now and to let things flow from there
Suited to	Adult breathers
Best for	Taking stock, creating awareness and letting go
Outcome	Gratitude, free of resistance of the present moment

Try your best and then let go. Expect nothing from anything but to be here now. Then now will flow into now. The future becomes a chain of *right now* moments connected to now. Like the concentric rings created by a large stone thrown into a pool. *Now* ripples through the flow. Breathe in slowly and toss a big stone into the pond. Don't create a splash – just enough for a stir. Attend to the little concentric ripples of now with one conscious breath at a time.

Be faithful to and grateful for your conscious breath and it will prepare the ground for your growth and awakening. The Buddha states, 'The road to enlightenment starts and finishes with the breath.'

Breathe, rest in being, and contain it with a smile of gratitude.

Chapter 32

On Work.
And Breath.

In work and life there is a time to follow, a time to lead, and a place beyond where we know the flow and we go with it.

To breathe is a wonderful metaphor for this passage. We can quietly observe and follow the breath in a meditative waking up stage; we can consciously watch and adapt the breath to empower a situation, and then we can simply let go in the glorious exhale. The breath has it all. There really is nothing to do but consciously breathe.

When you are the follower, be alert to where you put your attention. Be alert to how you consciously plant and seed the raised bed of your mind. Don't follow the crowd – follow the less-travelled path that leads to inspiration and truth. Seek out underived and authentic voices; you will know them when you hear them. They flow from the heart. It is important to go directly to the source of something, to honour it, and to listen. Everything else is second hand. Learn directly from there. You know the truth in your body when it comes your way.

When you are the leader, responsibility becomes your privilege and your cross. Being a responsive leader (not a reactive one) is so important. Leadership is not an easy job, but it is very flattering to the ego and so is something that on the outward journey of life, our egos can seek out for their enhancement. On reflection, mine did. Coming out of college with qualifications in the new field I was entering, I thought I was oven-ready for my chosen career. But I wasn't, because that was just college stuff completely outside the reality of the daily cut and thrust of the workplace. We are only truly ready to lead when all entitlement completely goes, and we are doing the job as a service to others rather than to ourselves and our CVs.

The corporate world is often organised around the survival of the fittest. This often means the survival of the fittest ego and, in many organisations, the fittest ego gets to the top. In a recent study into narcissism, they found the greatest concentration of narcissists was in the boardrooms of many of the top companies.[24] Unfortunately, when they are running the show everyone else gets stuck in a toxic workplace. Like attracts like and so corporate misery is perpetuated. If you find yourself working in this situation, and it becomes overwhelming, the solution is often self-preservation and to get out quickly.

One of the greatest leaders I can think of in my lifetime was an accidental one, Thich Nhat Hanh. A quiet, unassuming Vietnamese Zen Buddhist monk who may never have sought out the role. He was an author, poet, artist, peace walker, friend, monk, and head of a monastery, and if that wasn't enough, he introduced mindfulness to the Western world. He was also deeply principled and in the time of the Vietnam War risked his life to speak out about the conditions in his country while on a lecture tour of the USA. He had the most beautiful smile which came from the soles of his feet, just like some of the children at work. Through his practice he became simple, and his smile led the way home. Leadership flowed from this reluctant leader. His leadership was pure being in flow and an exquisite counterpoint to the narcissism found in boardrooms.

Leading happens one relationship at a time. You can start to bring out the best in others once you have first tried to bring out the best in yourself. Being recognises being, whereas ego is blind. An organisation trapped in ego is a competitive, unhappy place. Ego-based organisations are of the past. Purposeful organisations rooted in being and their own flow are of the present. When you are in a state of being, you are more sympathetic and open; you recognise the natural aliveness and space in yourself and so give this to others. The organisation becomes more organic because people start to operate from a place of greater awareness. Mistakes are encouraged as a sign that new things are being tried and they provide the opportunity for growth and reflection. A good idea doesn't mind who has it – and in this way, people are free to contribute without any fear.

When people are in a state of fear, they are unwittingly trapped in ego and are unable to freely contribute. Fear is toxic – to feel fear in a work context means we are not being properly supported or nurtured. Leaders who create a climate of fear are imposing on a situation and getting the worst out of everybody.

Anxiety is the first cousin of fear – worry is the second cousin. If you find yourself in these states, just smile in gratitude for your self-awareness and take a conscious breath. As you learn to take a conscious breath randomly throughout the day, you check in with yourself, with your inner state, and you help yourself to become.

To lead is to take responsibility. We are not in a state of reaction to the dramas that inevitably unfold. We move to response from reaction when we operate from being – and from drama to understanding when we give ourselves the space to be and reflect. Leading does not have to be upfront, in full view; it can be quiet and undemonstrative like Thich Nhat Hanh. When a leader leads from being they are in touch with flow and generally respond to a situation as required. Often a light touch on the rudder is all that it takes. If direct action and direct management is needed, and if it comes from being, then this will generally be correct for the organisation.

When an organisation has a strong purpose, whether it is widely stated or not, alignment with that purpose makes it flow. Organisations that work to directly support people are lucky in this regard. When the focus of the organisation becomes a genuine response to the people it serves, it will flow. Organisations that serve people have a built-in autopilot – just be and go from there, and if they go off-course, return to their being and go again. Most organisations have the capacity to be cynical too, and in this way, programmes which aim to explicitly change the culture of an organisation, without focusing on core values of being, are likely to fail because they will be met with resistance.

There is a quiet form of management, more like role modelling, where leaders are and show others how to be. An organisation will not evolve purely because you have made explicit plans for it. It will evolve because people in it are waking up, and from this space, others flow and become. When we met the authenticity of the children at work with our own, the school aligned with its deeper purpose. Although this sounds simple, it takes shared awareness of organisational purpose and culture, which grows over time. Planning for the future is possibly less significant when organisations become more conscious.

There are essentially two models that the person in charge can adopt when running an organisation. The first is leadership and the second is management. The word 'leader' suggests guiding and modelling, and a sense of direction. Whereas 'manager', sounds more like oversight, guidance and control. Leading is more about going with the flow and is more feminine in nature; managing implies intervention and input and can be more masculine. I recognise that my approach changed from one to the other either side of Covid.

To be in flow, a leader can be from alignment with the organisation and let things happen more organically from that space whereas a manager suggests being effortful and having to cut against the grain more. Whilst both roles can operate from being, once the person has woken up to the unconscious drives of their ego, the term 'leadership' is more sympathetic to flow. This is mentioned in the book, *Leading from the Emerging Future* by Otto Scharmer and Katrin Kaufer. They describe the paradigm shift from ego-systems to eco-systems and talk about the three openings that are required to transform systems: open mind, open heart and open will. These three openings essentially flow from presence, and in that space, organisations are more responsive to flow states.[25]

We become inspired not just through our breath but also by access to other people who are inspired and have accessed being. When people are inspired, they have a better chance to operate from the right understanding and do the right thing without the need for explicit guidance. They are trusted to be. In an ideal world, organisations start to create the conditions from which people are more and more available to respond fully to a situation without ego involvement. When people's egos get out of the way, there is a kind of collective choreography. The organisation dances – not to anyone's tune – but to the life which pulses through it.

Positivity creates positivity and people get on board. A positive virtuous cycle develops. The organisation starts to attract the right people and becomes a struggle for those whose egos oppose it. More and more people who are aligned with the core values are attracted to being there whilst those who remain become more conscious of them. People no longer need to cut against the grain anymore and work becomes less effortful, less like work. When there are enough people working from being or being inspired by it, the organisation takes on a life of its own. As people have the space to be, they become more spontaneous and helpful. Fear erodes and people are freer to take risks. New leaders emerge, like flowers from the raised bed, and they go on to inspire others.

Responsibility is a big part of leadership. But the right path is often not clear. When you see the big picture, you often become less sure about anything. You need space to process things to discern the way. Here we return to the great unknowing where wisdom grows by opening to the truth of not knowing. In the modern world, not having an instant answer or reaction goes against the grain of the switched-on culture. But it is important to understand what people are switched onto. Generally, it is the jibber-jabber of the mind which is amplified online. The truth gets quickly drowned out in this context. So, it is more important than ever to have time to discern the right path if you are in a leadership role. Pause. Breathe. Sleep on it. Do whatever you can to give yourself the time and space to access the truth that emanates from being.

The truth is that rarely do decisions need to be made instantly. The conditions when a right answer comes from a reactive state are rare; these are often our chimp's domain and based on primal needs for self-preservation. We realise that we don't need to struggle anymore – we just need to respond to a situation from a space of being. That is the deep essence of an understanding of responsibility – or better still, 'response-ability', when right action flows from right mind.

When we stop struggling with our ego we can let go into the flow. Sometimes this happens in our life, and we become free here now, but more often it happens in death, where we finally know from the experience in front of us that we are not our body or our ego. This is not a question of faith; there have been many reports of near-death experiences which document very similar passages of events just before people feel called back to re-enter the body. Anybody who sees and knows this mystery in life has woken up and is able to be free here now.

Beyond the cycle of following, egoic leadership and natural leadership is flow. It is the place of quiet surrender where we rest in the being of our heart and let it all be. We are done with doing and just flow with the tide, the Tao of life. There is no more following or leading to be done. This can be a stepping back in an organisational context or in life; we just stop struggling with everything and move on from a difficult phase or situation.

◯ Let's breathe

Breathing space	The Leadership Breath
Duration	30 seconds
Response	To centre my thoughts and awaken my senses
Best for	Modelling in team connections; being visible
Outcome	Share positivity

The more we consciously and visibly breathe as a leader, the more we will give space and permission to colleagues to step up. Try and model nasal breathing as this much more naturally emanates containment and flow. In this way, we reach rapport more quickly and are open to the wonderful possibility of not knowing.

Even better than modelling it, organise it. Arrange times for colleagues to be in silence together. Just before a meeting is ideal. Simply breathe together. Just fifteen to thirty seconds of this is enough to start.

We all have responsibilities towards other people. Make a list of yours here. Can you split them into two columns: one where you are managing, and the other where you are leading? Now take a few consecutive conscious breaths. Are your lists aligned as you would wish? Are there some things that you are currently managing where you could let go a little and be more of a leader?

Breathe, rest in being, and smile.

Chapter 33

Impulse Control

It is a shame it took me so long to wise up.

I was totally unsuited to office life. I needed my own set of calm-down cards but it would be another twenty years or so until I discovered them. I have never got the comedy *The Office*, possibly because I found it too close to the mark. My life in an office was like that: slow, excruciating workdays, with forced relationships, endlessly recycling unnecessary jobs in the pursuit of some faraway corporate goal. The blandness of it and the prescribed regularity of it all left me feeling hopeless. Was this what life had in store for me?

So, I quit. I remember the day I handed in my notice. On the last day, I literally ran out of the building. We were on the ninth floor of the office block. The lift was too slow so I ran down the fire stairs. I ran out the building and down the road to the bus stop and jumped up to grab on to the roof of the bus shelter and hang down. I stretched to swing from the top of it. This was quite unusual behaviour from a young man in an ever-increasingly tight blue suit on Hammersmith Broadway. In truth, as time went on from the moment of pedestrian ceremony, I substituted this office for another one, with better perks and travel. It was a little freer, but it was another office, and it still felt like I was squeezing into my suit and the walls of the office were my cage.

It wasn't working, this new job, so I had to break out (again). Something had to be done. I quit the city, sold my flat, headed for the hills of the Lake District, and trained as a primary school teacher. It worked. Looking back, I don't regret the drama of it, per se. I needed to experience the rapid high and wretched discomfort of it all. I would, however, have opted to revise that bus shelter stunt, probably.

Was I being responsive or reactive at the bus shelter? I have asked myself this question many a time. I'm sure the bus drivers on the drive-by must have asked this too. The answer of course is reactive.

Reactive behaviour has no respect for timing. One of the most important lessons in any organisation is about timing – that is, knowing when to wait for the right time to say something or to resign or to run away. It's become a performance indicator not to be reactive to every message, conversation or emotional release. I failed that one, dismally. The response to a crisis does not have to be as dramatic as upping sticks and heading for the hills either. Maybe if I had discovered breathwork then, I might have navigated it all differently. It certainly may have been wiser to start my journey with a deep breath, rather than swinging from the bus stop in Hammersmith Broadway.

Choosing less drama would have been more 'me', but it felt as if I was escaping and had to claim my freedom. Less drama would have been a more conscious response to the impulse. But on the day I ran out of the building, I felt as if I had solved all my problems. I hadn't, of course. But in the sheer release, the bus shelter became my escape hatch. It could have been the nearest pub, or an act of insanity. Being able to introduce an element of choice, space (grace) and awareness into how we respond dramatically changes the choices we make and our life's outcomes.

As we breathe consciously, we start to bring awareness to something that our body does unconsciously. We connect mind and body and over time this connection gets stronger and more established. It becomes a more familiar route that is more fluent and automatic. As this develops, we start to see the benefits of conscious breathing, and so do it more often. A virtuous cycle begins. The mind loves a habit, so the path of conscious breathing gets slowly embedded.

Life is complex. Often hard, we know. And there will be many times we are called to impulse. Oftentimes we catch ourselves telling friends how we lost our minds in a moment; most of these conversations end with a good laugh and a pat on the back. But what is really happening when we 'lose it', and when we are in a moment of severe impulse? When we lose it, we have essentially lost a sense of being, and start to identify so much with our mind-made states that we become them. What I lost at the bus stop was my prefrontal cortex, and what I found swinging from the shelter was my chimp.

These mind-made states seem so real, but they are not. They are merely our ego creating momentum for itself, which can be so convincing and pervasive and hard to break free of. In ego we have no joy and peace; we are cut off from our true selves. The Buddha calls this state 'Dukkha', translated as 'suffering' or 'unhappiness'.

The mind-made, man-made, states of fear, anxiety, anger and despair start to be seen for what they are after a period of conscious breathing. They are not the ultimate reality of who you are. As you feel these states, take a conscious breath. When we experience them, however all-consuming they feel, they are a sign that we have become distanced from our source of self and are an opportunity for return and growth. When we respond to unknown triggers and impulses, it is as if a foreigner has taken the wheel of our car and we are no longer in control. *We have lost it.* We become defined by our reaction to the situation and lose flow. Sometimes losing it is obvious to all, but generally and more subtly, losing it has us circling around and around in endless spirals of thought – spirals of worry, doubt, fear and anxiety. This becomes compulsive, brings us no peace, and is not our natural state of being.

When an autistic child lost their way at school, they could quite simply 'lose it', which became very clear to everybody. The children were honest, and the socially conditioned filter which neurotypical adults learn had not always been fully developed. Colleagues were trained to watch carefully, and as a relationship developed, impulses and triggers could be anticipated, and panic and escalated events could generally be prevented. When a situation escalated despite everything, safety was paramount. When the student was not available to hear, we just gave time: time to be, time to be with them, and time to say nothing. Even a request like 'take a deep breath' could not be heard; rather, it could be another trigger, so we needed to model it. We needed to be what we needed them to be – and to act the way we wanted them to act. So we breathed out loud with big breaths that could be heard and felt.

What is primarily sensed and heard by a child in crisis is our breath and our presence. The elemental truth of a crisis distils the needs down to just breath and heart. I know this as I have seen the conscious use and modelling of breath and presence to defuse a crisis so many times. By breathing consciously and audibly we made no demands; we were physically present and signalling that we would not add words to a situation which needed to be calmed. If someone can't de-escalate by breathing deeply, breathe deeply for them. If they can't sigh, sigh for them.

At work, as the children became more self-aware and developed emotional literacy, they were asked to feed back on the emotional state or zone they were in. Seeing is freeing for us all, so once they recognised the emotional zone they were in, they knew what path they were on and what interventions or calm-down choices could support them. With training and practice they started to take this path to support their emotions in the moment and often pick breathing exercises from a few calm-down cards presented to them.

If the breath works for neurodivergent children in a crisis, it will surely work for you. With this knowledge we can explore the Let Go Breath. The breath of letting go is a long audible exhale, that stills the moment, and it can be modelled. When we breathe consciously, and audibly, we emanate energetic positivity. The electromagnetic field of the heart is five hundred times stronger than the head; by emanating and radiating peace from our heart, everything, literally everything, can change. And the children felt this.

By making the connection between mind and body, we start to re-route ourselves. We see the truth of who we really are and who we are not. We disidentify with our thoughts and sense a stillness which emanates from source energy. From here things flow. As we become more conscious with conscious breathing, the right choices and the right paths open. The bridge we have built between our mind and body leads us home. As we start to take this journey home, the old ego routes start to recede in prominence, and we see the right path. Our being has taken the wheel and knows the route and the potholes on the way. In this state, triggers are understood for what they are, and we are no longer in a state of constant reaction. We steer the right course and impulses are correctly interpreted so that the impulse–thought–reaction–thought feedback loop is broken and no longer runs us. We are safe and everything is understood for what it is. We have made that massive transition of shifting from reaction to response, and in so doing, we claim our freedom.

The implications of this are even bigger than claiming our freedom – once we have, we have a responsibility to help. As we move from a reactive state to a responsive one, we become free of all the programmes that have run us for years. When our own bridges are built, we have the awareness to help others across their own. We can emanate the breath of being, sometimes by breathing audibly, and so reassure others that out there is a place of peace and joy and calm. In this way, conscious breathing becomes a practice not just for us but for the world.

◯ Let's breathe

Breathing space	The Generous Breath
Duration	60 seconds
Response	Calming of crisis
Suited to	Parent–child, stressful or impulsive interactions
Best for	Autistic children and impulsive reaction
Outcome	Mirror breathing; finding stillness in the noise

These days when I encounter something huge and unfathomable, I try to be and breathe audibly. It doesn't always work, as I found in the forests of Portugal, but by breathing audibly, and trying to emanate peace to those around me, I give the situation my best shot.

Take a generous breath from time to time. When you see

someone in crisis or encounter people under stress, hold space and breathe for them. Take a conscious breath now, breathe and sigh out loud, breathe audibly. Breathe with control. Stay steady. Let the room hear you.

Breathe, rest in being, and smile.

Chapter 34

Chain Reactions

Our day flows moment to moment. Now to now.

There is no future or past, just as we can't breathe in the future or the past. We can only breathe now. Now is linked to now just as breath is linked to breath.

Our day builds breath by breath just as writing builds sentence by sentence. One conscious breath is now. The next one is now. Each breath is linked to another. Like elephants walking trunk to tail, the line of elephants is built one elephant at a time. When the breath flows freely and is connected to the next one without a pause on the inhale or the exhale, it is called conscious connected breathing (CCB), and is one of the most powerful transformational breathing practices.

In CCB the exhale creates the opportunity for the inhale and then flows again – trunk to tail, trunk to tail. We consciously build positivity when we consciously link our breathing, breath to breath. This becomes a virtuous chain reaction. Under the guidance of a qualified breath worker who embodies the breath we need and holds a safe space for our growth, resistance starts to erode and we flow with the breath.

Habitually, the flow of awareness from moment to moment, breath to breath, becomes interrupted – particularly when we get disturbed. If this disturbance goes unchecked, we can become unconscious and return to our ego. When we return to ego, a negative chain reaction is more possible. As an example, I had a personal experience which followed a particularly challenging conversation at work. I could not stay conscious through the process and found myself being defensive and operating from my ego. I remained in this state for a few hours and on the way home went to the garage to get four new tyres for my car. The mechanic gave out to me that it was too late to bring a car in for so many tyres on a Friday afternoon, but he eventually agreed to do it and asked me to return later. I went for a walk in the nearby park and found myself daydreaming a bit and strayed onto the cycle path. This provoked a strong verbal reaction and gesture from a cyclist who was behind me, yelling at me to get out of the cycle lane. These events felt quite rare and I wondered if they were in any way connected.

As I walked and consciously breathed, I understood that *I* was the problem. I was angry from the meeting at work and let the energy from that go unchecked. It would have been far better if I had taken time and responsibility for how I felt after the first incident and broken the chain rather than entrenching myself in it. One of the best ways for me is to physically remove myself from the situation, get out in the fresh air and do a short breath walk to calm down. But I didn't. The anger remained with me and I stayed unconscious and negative and brought that into my next meeting at the garage. This negativity was further reinforced by our encounter over the closing time, and shortly after I was shouted at for walking on the wrong path. Although each were quite small incidents, three in a row in quick succession was a lot. I had to become more conscious to break the chain.

A little while later I returned to the garage, with a slightly new mindset and a little more in the present moment. The mechanic was fitting the last of the four tyres and smiled. I thanked him, paid, and we had a positive conversation about our weekend ahead. The chain was broken for me, and it was broken for him. When we move from reaction to response in this way, we start to operate from the energy of the heart, and the chain breaks.

We do not have a problem as much as the problem has us. But when we choose our response, we empower ourselves rather than being stuck in a knee-jerk reaction to it. When we respond rather than react to something, we have its measure and transform it.

The mind is quick to dart onto a problem, fix it and embellish it. It likes problems and fixing them because it gives the impression that it is in control. It may even create them, so we get caught in a web of its making. Making space is the answer, and this can be done with just one conscious breath. When we introduce space to any situation, we give ourselves the opportunity to pause, take stock and choose our response from the heart.

When we become more conscious, we break a chain of negativity and start to build moments of positivity. This is done like links in the chain of now – moment to moment, trunk to tail, trunk to tail. We cannot change what happens to us now, but we can change our response to it. By changing our response, we change our life's outcomes.

◯ Let's breathe

Breathing space	Walking Reset Breath
Duration	10 minutes
Response	Calming of crisis
Suited to	Parents; times of conflict or confusion
Best for	Calming down, breaking the chain, and getting a fresh perspective
Outcome	Letting go; seeing with fresh eyes

How often have you heard: 'I am just heading out for a walk'? It's always a good idea, especially when its intentional and removes us from a situation that cannot be resolved in the present moment, or when we need to let off some steam.

Just one thing though, as you walk try to nasal breathe and consciously extend your inhale. That will help to both centre you and help you let go. Focus on the breath and not your problem. That way, at the end of the walk the problem may have resolved itself.

Breathe, rest in being, and smile.

Chapter 35

Goals

'When the mind serves the heart, anything is possible, although when the heart serves the mind, there is perpetual limitation.'

– Glenda Green

Growing up, I had the goal to make as much money as possible.

I had fully absorbed the acquisitive culture of the time, got educated for it with a degree in marketing, and intended to take my place. Marketing as a discipline was developed in America in the fifties and sixties and had come to Europe. There were just a couple of colleges offering it in England at the time as a graduate programme, and it seemed to be a route to get rich quick.

One of the earliest modules was on business planning. One school of thought was that an organisation could be whatever it wanted to be once it had put plans in place. The targets that drove the planning process were fiscal ones of income, growth, profit and market share. The way to reach them was to follow the plan. The plan was everything, and all the measurable objectives and targets were made explicit.

Within certain organisations, key individual workers were then incentivised and rewarded for reaching their targets. This would be reviewed annually in the light of the previous year's figures and increased accordingly. Growth compounded growth and an exponential growth in profits offered the possibility of exponential growth in pay packets. This wasn't a problem as such because most people bought into the culture of perpetual growth and so it was deemed to be a good thing all round – it was understood as a corporate win and a personal win. Yes, we may have all been speeding up, but this was alright since everyone with a stake got richer and richer. Except we weren't. Not everyone had a stake, and as our knowledge of interdependencies and ecology deepened, a broader and more inclusive definition of success emerged which started to include and embrace the welfare of the individual and the environment.

The core problem with planning is that it is trying to envision a future and so takes us out of the present moment. If it is solely done with the thinking mind it will limit our intuitions which happen when we tap into flow.

Despite transitioning my career from head of marketing to primary school teacher, letting go of an earlier life was difficult. My ego secretly wanted people to acknowledge the financial sacrifices I had made, and it was only later that I managed to disidentify with this.

Up to quite recently I would plan my day, make lists of things to do, and get a disproportionate sense of achievement when I crossed them off. The crossing off of an item became a target itself. In this way, the tendency can still be to be driven by the end goal rather than how it is achieved.

Twenty-five years later I know that some of the most important things in life can't be put on a list. These are depth dimensions that include: consciousness, attention, listening, authenticity, and creativity, and are by far the most important things we bring to our work – but just try crossing them off a list!

Multitasking is a bit of a buzz concept but when we multitask, we multitask our attention and become future-oriented. Multitasking masks the moment of now by burying us in the multifaceted stuff in front of us. It prevents us from being present and here. In the future, work may embrace a paradigm shift from working for extrinsic goals of perceived success and profit to intrinsic and less tangible ways of being. Work will be less about what we do and more about who we are. This is because when our work flows from our heart, the fruits of our *it* are aligned and everything starts to fall into place. I love the story of the four Zen monks comparing the depth of their masters. The final one concludes that his master was the greatest because he did the dishes. He brought less doing and more being to all his activities, however mundane. This reminds us that all our activities, no matter their importance, are important – everything is of equal value in the present moment because it is now and deserves the same level of dignity. Incidentally, another definition of Zen is doing one thing at a time.

By being in being, we lift the pressure from our shoulders and our minds, and we settle in the knowing of the heart. Breathe consciously as often as you can – and you return to this knowing of the heart, where life starts to take care of itself, free of your meddling mind.

◯ Let's breathe

Breathing reflection

When the mind serves the heart, anything is possible. So take a little time now to just sit with your heart. Feel it beat. This is going to lead you home. As it beats, slowly align your breath. Six beats on the inhale, and six beats on the exhale. If a thought pops into your mind, smile in gratitude for the opportunity to breathe consciously again. Do this for a minute or so, or whatever feels comfortable. As your familiarity with this technique develops, explore taking it into a full reflective practice. You can develop this further by looking at Coherent Breathing in the appendix (p267).

Chapter 36

You Are Your Own Problem

We increase the experience of stress when we are not here and want to be there.

This is where goal setting can inadvertently go wrong, when we allow future goals to fuel an overthinking mind. When we are looking out into the future, we are projecting into a time that doesn't exist now. It might be when we return home after a tough day at work, or when we retire to the perceived elixir of not working, a holiday, getting the deposit together to buy a house, a new relationship, winning the lotto, an evening out, the end of physical pain and illness, or paying off debt. Whatever the end of the telescope is, it is taking us out of the now. The key is to set an intention and to keep it on ice, so to speak, while you stay working in the present moment. We cannot solve a problem of the mind in the mind alone – to solve a problem of the mind we need to be guided by our heart, where our most profound intelligence resides. But if we keep our mind on the problem, the perceived solution becomes just more mind and more problem.

In presenting the apparent solution to our problems, the ego subtly further entrenches us in identification with the problem or the goal and prevents us from seeing the wood from the trees. It is a bit like having a drink to relax, unaware of the cumulative anxiety that our long-term drinking can cause. The solution is not someplace else; it is here now. In the now there is no need to worry about the future because solutions will flow from us being in the now, now. The ego is very deceptive in this way – it does not want to be found out as it cannot coexist with being in the present moment. So it sets targets for us. But don't worry – seeing the ego is the start of being free of it.

We are all human, and encounter stress. I found myself becoming stressed around an IT issue this week. I did not grow up in the period of computing, and it doesn't come naturally to me. There was a problem with a business app this week which had morphed my identity with my partner's, and I was not able to communicate with anyone on the app as a result. I did not have a record of what was happening anymore. Part of the problem, particularly with issues that take us out of our comfort zone, is recognising them and framing the issues clearly and neutrally, free of emotion. This becomes very difficult when we identify with the stress that it is causing us and so want to sort it out as soon as possible. When we can frame something neutrally, we are literally halfway to finding the solution because we can now invite people in to help us sort it out.

At the beginning of the week, I could not do this because I had overidentified with the perceived hardship that it was causing me and so desperately needed a solution. I communicated this desire through a lack of clarity and frustration, and as a result was met with the same lack of clarity. I had three unsuccessful calls, and my stress mounted. The confusion I was putting out there was being returned to me with interest.

183

Then one morning as I was walking, the penny dropped. I was so far out of my comfort zone and so in need of getting to the end point of this issue that I was loathing all the steps along the way. I was not in the moment at any moment of this, and my frustration was keeping people out. Being here now I was able to model the solution I needed. With this awareness I finally had a sense of empowerment. I formulated the problem more clearly in my head and approached the call centre with a perspective of trying to be in the process of jointly resolving the issue and accept the moment for what it was. As I changed my perspective, the energy around the problem changed and my encounters with the call centre staff improved; they heard my problem clearly and were reassuring and positive that we would find a solution to the issue now. The clarity that I belatedly put out there was now returned to me. And we did resolve the issue. *Together.*

I realised just how well-trained the call centre staff were. They were there to help me, but being stressed projected me into a desired solution and in so doing I was resisting all the steps along the way.

Many situations trigger stress and include times when we are:
- doing something the ego doesn't like,
- working too hard too long,
- physical overwhelm,
- looking back (or forward) in rose-tinted spectacles to an idealised time and place, and
- focusing so much on the need to find a solution we miss the steps on the way.

The answer to our perceived problems is to accept what is and be here now: just one conscious breath can mark the start of a return to ourselves – and puts down the welcome mat for others to come in and help us out.

Of course, this is easier said than done, especially when we are in stress because the very nature of stress obscures everything else and has us chasing around the circus ring for a solution. By obscuring the problem, the potential for a solution is concealed and we are robbed of our power.

Stress creates a reactive and disempowered state. Any egoic interference with a process creates resistance which blocks the natural flow of finding the solution. To uncover a solution in flow, we must let go of this identification and be here now. We become entrenched in our own problem through complete identification with the need for a solution. As we do this, we create more stress, which distances us further from our ability to be here now, and so the problem compounds itself entirely of our own making. Unless we can break the chain with awareness and right intention, vicious cycles spin on and on. When we understand that we are always our own problem, the simple solution is revealed, which is just to stop and be present. With this right mind and right intention in the present moment, issues will resolve themselves as if on their own.

A question I have found useful when some of the children were stressed was, 'Wait, can you just check if you are breathing?' When they did this, it returned them to their breath and away from their issues and opened a small gap in their awareness. Recognising that we are in a state of stress, we are halfway there and so have the possibility of returning to ourselves with a few more conscious breaths. Through conscious breathing we can return to ourselves and the chance to move from the despair of reaction to the empowerment of response.

As self-awareness of the inner state develops through conscious breathing, we look for it more and more. Conscious breathing creates a virtuous circle of creating self-awareness to recognise the need for more of it. If you find yourself in stress, just take one conscious breath. Get out of your head and be here now. Like a computer, turn yourself off and on again; give yourself a reboot and see how you feel.

In Ireland there is very little time for people who brag about ego accomplishments or who see themselves as important. In groups you will hear comments like, 'Would he ever get over himself?' 'See the head on him,' and 'He's completely lost the run of himself,' for anyone who is heading in this direction. Any accomplishment is more properly met with self-deprecatory humour.

In embracing with clarity that we are our own problem, we can embrace self-deprecation; we can accept our stuff. We 'lighten up' and 'get over ourselves' and we don't 'completely lose the run.' We become more honest and own our stuff, which is a big step to the eventual surrender to the flow of life.

◯ Let's breathe

Breathing space	The Get Over Yourself Breath
Duration	30 seconds
Response	To centre my thoughts and awaken my senses
Best for	Self-enquiry; clearing the decks and going again
Outcome	Clarity; cutting through the crap; wisdom

Ask yourself, 'What is my inner state now? Am I in peace or am I in stress?' Remember, seeing is freeing. Recognise how you are, and if you are in stress, take one conscious breath to kick off the process of altering your inner state. Alternatively, if you are in peace, take one conscious breath in gratitude. Either way, the response to how you are feeling right now is just one conscious breath. So do it now in gratitude.

Don't stress. Be here now, and be open to let go with the flow.

Breathe, rest in being, and smile.

Chapter 37

Breathing
for Burnout

We experience burnout when we feel so physically and emotionally overwhelmed and overworked that we cannot function properly.

Some work environments, particularly in the corporate world, are so unnaturally competitive and dedicated to the cause that they create a kind of corporate arms race where workers feel compelled to work beyond the point of exhaustion because everyone else is. This fuels a culture of burnout, and the survival of the fittest becomes a company badge of endurance.

Burnout in caring professions is different but equally felt; when people are always on and continually giving to others, they can become burned out from their constant availability to helping people at the very deepest level.

Burnout also happens in the complexity of our many life and care roles and the increasing blurring of these boundaries. This is further exacerbated by being constantly online, pulling previously defined boundaries out of shape, merging and fusing them at the edges in the process. This was clearly seen during the pandemic, when being online helped pull us through as we juggled everything from home. But in the process, there was an even deeper blurring of the boundaries, as working from home morphed into living at work. When such fundamental boundaries start to slide, the sanctuary of our personal space is compromised, leaving us less sure of ourselves in our own homes.

In her book *The Art of Enough*, Becky Hall, a life coach and author, writes about people she worked with during the pandemic who came to understand that what they were being asked to do was impossible.[26] Rather than being misinterpreted as a statement of failure, this was seen as a recognition of the cliff edge – an unsustainable place that had to be turned back from.

Saying 'no' or 'enough' at this point kept her clients safe and sane. With this understanding they were encouraged to let go of some roles and reframe others to find a new way that was enough. The establishment of clear boundaries became a protective factor against burnout. For the increasingly complex future we all face into, our boundaries need to evolve so we can cope.

Our reality is at least three dimensional and with the emergence of artificial intelligence is getting much more challenging. The problem is our boundaries tend to be two dimensional. It's like trying to stem a torrential flood of overwhelm with a pile of sticks. Something deeper is needed to stem the tide. Only the depth of awareness comprehends the depth of the problem. By cultivating this through a reflective practice and the inner spaciousness that this opens, we begin to create the awareness to meet the flood of overwhelm. This can start with just one conscious breath.

Starting with our one conscious breath, we create space for pause and rest in the moment here now. With this prompt and rest, we temporarily stop the wheels from turning and slowly, slowly start to see the solution for ourselves.

In burnout, desperation and depletion happens because there is insufficient time for relaxation and rest. The body is perpetually exhausted so continually calls for energy from the sympathetic nervous system. But this compounds the experience of burnout. As the body keeps sending emergency signals to the organs, readying them for action, they do, so over time we become drained. The energy that is used up here is like a sugar fix, a quick hit with a terrible downside, and the only solution becomes another hit to stave off the crash.

A vast amount of the nerves that stimulate the sympathetic nervous system are at the top of our lungs. Quick shallow breathing, which is what we do when we are exhausted or in panic, switches on the sympathetic nervous system and bingo, another sugar hit kicks in. When the body is crying 'full house', it is really experiencing the start of another vicious sugar cycle.

In burnout we become trapped in the system and forget about ourselves. When we are without awareness, we repeat the old coping mechanism of overcompensation by ramping up the dials, distancing us further and further from our true selves. Once again, unhealthy coping mechanisms entrench us in the problem. As this process continues unconsciously for an extended period, we accelerate burnout.

The type of energy we have in burnout is highly adrenalised. We feel wired like a constant caffeine high. If you find yourself constantly rushing around, then nine times out of ten you are drawing on adrenalised energy from your sympathetic nervous system, which, if used unconsciously for a long period, causes inflammation and long-term damage to health. Awareness is key: become aware of your breath and how it corresponds to the energy you have. Just one conscious breath slows us down and makes us aware of what's going on.

Our body is not able to differentiate between a thought and a thing. A threat is a threat irrespective of source. So, it is no surprise in the modern always-on culture that we are becoming completely drained. To understand this process better, let's look at an extreme situation: in warfare. Fighters on the front line work from a hypervigilant, always-on state. When asleep, any sound could be a bomb – it is impossible to differentiate between a bomb exploding or a door closing firmly. When in battle, a soldier's sympathetic nervous system is always on, and they get little time to rest and recover.

A powerful example I like to offer in cases of burnout is the combat method of the Navy SEALs. The Navy SEALs worked with a breath worker and learned to practise successive rounds of Box Breathing together in combat.[27] Rather like a box, Box Breathing has four equal sides. These correspond to the length of an inhale, pause, exhale, and pause. It is often practised in counts of three or four and is explored in greater depth at the back of this book. Box Breathing stimulates a relaxed yet alert state, the ideal state of being on and ready but not drained. This is the opposite of burnout breathing, which is the fast shallow breaths spoken about. As a community, the Navy SEALs wait in a relaxed yet attentive state. There is that phrase again. Being relaxed and alert flows from the parasympathetic nervous system, which is the holy grail of combat and is the holy grail for navigating our way through life. Regular sustained practice of Box Breathing stimulates the parasympathetic nervous system, which is a wonderful support against burnout. It also shifts the mindset from reaction to response.

Here's the scary thing: if in sleep Navy SEALs are unable to differentiate between a bomb going off and a door closing, we are not able to differentiate between a deep shock and a WhatsApp message pinging in the middle of the night. Getting rest has never been so fraught. It's really no surprise that in their perpetual on and stimulated state, children are more anxious today than ever before. We must take responsibility and set boundaries for rest, for us and our children. If we don't do this, no one else will. Whatever the route to burnout, there is a common feeling of despair and insurmountable stress. We have a sensation of running on empty and draining the emergency tanks. It's as if our well of contentment and calm has been completely drained and we feel desperate. Press the pause button and take a conscious breath.

◯ Let's breathe

Breathing space	The Box Breath
Duration	Three minutes
Response	To centre my thoughts, balance my nervous system and create relaxed alertness
Best for	Moments of stress; times we need to be relaxed yet focused
Outcome	Balance; relaxed alertness

Stress and burnout are closely related. Stress is not being here now because we have our sights on there – and burnout is despite being physically here, we can't be because we're just too exhausted. The answer to both is to be present in the moment and this can start with just one conscious breath. This will indicate your need for deeper rest.

We initiate the pause at the start of the inhale and complete it in the space following the exhale. Re-engaging after a pause helps us to return to where we were in a slightly new and spacious way. The opening of space is a protective factor against the flood of overwhelm in this digital age.

If you get the sense of being completely exhausted, box breathe (see appendix, p269) or breathe low and slow into the bottom of your lungs. This way you will access the nerves that stimulate the parasympathetic nervous system.

Breathe, rest in being, and smile.

Chapter 38

Pressing Pause

So much of our life is spent waiting.

In a culture of constant work and productivity, waiting can be viewed as unproductive time that needs to be filled. Just look around. Everyone is busy *not* waiting – occupying their time and their minds with screens or something, anything. It seems that everyone is busy not being by being on screens. It is as if nothing must always be filled with *something*. It doesn't. Nothing is wonderful. Think of the beautiful deciduous tree standing bare in its skeletal form in winter; it is still and just waiting for the seasons to change so it can blossom again. Everything happens as nature intended in this state of waiting or calm dormancy.

I remember a long time ago when travelling in India, getting a ticket and then a berth for a long-distance train could take half a day. This was widely accepted and there was an atmosphere of collective calm. Meeting and talking with people during these times was a big part of the adventure. Likewise, recently I had an unexpected six-hour delay at Birmingham Airport. It enabled me to catch up with my writing after a busy weekend. I was alone and there were no demands on me so I spent the time consciously and slowly breathing through my nose. After fifteen minutes or so, I became my breath, and this continued for the next five to six hours as I practised. Everything else was outside and fine but was taking place a step or two away. I was fully present but detached. I felt my inner state become calm and centred, and my tiredness from burning the candle at both ends over the weekend receded. The delay and all time dissolved into the present. The turning of the tide of breath from out to in was all there was, like momentary beads of now, flowing in a chain.

After a while I started to observe things in a new, slightly heightened way: the colours around me took on a vividness and saturation as if the ink in my printer had been replaced; the lines of the architecture of the airport flowed from one space to the next. The chirrup of birds looking for a crumb of croissant, dusk, the beautiful vibrant turbans and headgear of fellow passengers boarding their flight to New Delhi, the kindness of people towards me, and the way we flowed through the departure gate together. As I became more in tune with my inner state, I was more in touch with the outer; everything embraced a vibrant and gentle peace.

There is no waiting when our body is home. As we consciously breathe our mindset shifts, we become more rooted in the present moment and less concerned with flying off to different destinations. I wasn't waiting at the airport, I was being. A deep peace seeded in my mind and body, and I flowed along with it as if consciously flowing on the breath of life.

There is a real pleasure in waiting, consciously, not being in a hurry, not being in a rush to fill our time with stuff. The Italians have a beautiful phrase for this exact state: *Il Belle Niente*, directly translated as 'the beautiful nothing'. The Italians have always been onto a good thing.

For me this time of conscious nasal breathing was simply trans-formative. I experienced a serenity and vivid aliveness through the transition. Rather than being delayed in my journey, I arrived home.

Breathe, rest in being. Smile. And sigh.

The art of doing nothing starts with accessing our breath. This is a place which I know I can return to. We all can. We enter the portal of now by taking a conscious breath. Yes, it isn't always just one conscious breath – but it is taking just one conscious breath at a time, and by doing this we stay in the present moment with every connected breath. We can only be present to this breath. We can't be present to a future breath or a past one. Each breath ripples the surface of the deep well of now. Drop them down consciously and watch – each breath is peace and joy; each breath is your birthright. Find your own truth and become your own researcher by taking many conscious breaths in sequence in the present moment. And watch. And be.

◯ Let's breathe

Breathing space	The Waiting Breath
Duration	As long as you need to train your patience
Response	To calm me down; make me grateful and go with it
Suited to	Impatient minds and hurried souls
Best for	Frustrating queues, traffic jams, and general delays
Outcome	Revived spirit; reconnecting with 'I am'

Just watch your breath come and go. It is a magical time to just be, not to do. Don't stimulate the sympathetic nervous system by constantly being on. Take the opportunity of the beautiful nothing, to breathe deeply, rest, and draw on the parasympathetic nervous system. Don't do distraction. Just wait, and be in that moment. Take a few conscious breaths and be with yourself. Wait patiently with yourself. When you are home to yourself, there is no waiting anymore. There is nowhere to go, nowhere to be but to be here now.

Take one conscious breath. Then continue for another three minutes until you rest in being. Taking responsibility is just that – your ability to respond to what happens – and it flows from moment to moment now. With awareness, you can break free of a negative chain developing and start to build positivity, moment to moment, breath to breath. You are starting a positive chain reaction.

The next time you feel a problem brewing, go out and breathe some fresh air. Be here now. Breathe. Rest in being. Smile. And sigh. You may see that with repeated practice of one conscious breath that you have already arrived.

Breathe, rest in being, and smile.

Chapter 39

Being and Flowing
in Meditation

Mantra meditation is a wonderful practice and is one
way to experience no-thing.

The word mantra comes from two Sanskrit words, '*manas*' (mind)
and '*tra*' (tool), so it translates as being a tool or instrument of the
mind. In Sanskrit the mantra '*rama*' is widely used. The best known
one is 'aum' (om). Earlier this was likened to the word 'home' – and
repeating it is like coming home to ourselves. This is described as the
primordial sound of the universe, and when repeated in silence chimes
three inner sounds. Some Buddhists use '*om mani padre hum*', which
refers to the sacred 'I' at the heart of the lotus. In Christian meditation,
which was quite recently rediscovered by the late John Main, the
phrase 'Maranatha' (come Lord Jesus) is offered.

Choosing a mantra is important; sometimes they are handed
down by teachers, and if you have a religious tradition, it is good to
pick one from there. Some mantras, in particular the ones from the

East, often have a natural resonance and are particularly good at training the mind. In Transcendental Meditation the mantras come from the ancient Vedic tradition of India. They are given to students by the instructor in a closed ceremony to repeat and practise faithfully twice daily.

I started practising Transcendental Meditation over thirty years ago. The practice and structure of this is a wonderful support. Yet I have come to see that attachment to a mantra and the act of 'doing' a meditation can become a kind of thought and activity that we can get attached to and find hard to let go of. The deepest essence of any meditation, and our deepest desire, is not to just do a meditation but to become it.

The role of a mantra is probably threefold in nature. Initially, it distracts us from our constant thought stream, then with practice it acts like a mental barrier, training the mind and keeping some external thoughts at bay, until eventually, at the deepest level, it drops away and leaves us silence and inner spaciousness. Earlier this was compared to being in a flow state. We become the meditation. Ultimately then we use the mantra to lose it – and arrive home to ourselves in our inner stillness and space. This is our true self. The space between our thoughts is free of jibber-jabber, and reflects our inner spaciousness. It will erode the stone of false self-identity – drop by drop, mantra by mantra, breath by breath.

It sometimes helps to syllabicate a mantra and coordinate this with the breath. Let's take 'Maranatha' as an example. It has four syllables: ma·ra·na·tha. Now take the first and the third syllables to correspond with the inhale, and the second and the fourth syllables the exhale. Breathe the sounds with the breath. This reduces the potential for distraction and helps the meditation flow. Combining a mantra and the breath in this way can be a very effective way to reach the no-thing at

199

our core. In Christian meditation, this no-thing at our core can be understood as reaching the love in our heart. Beyond that, and still part of it, is the universal energy of love, or God, that pervades everything.

There is nothing complicated about using a mantra to help breathe. The trick I have learned is to just *be* – just be in the same space where the mantra lets go and drops away. We are always this close to our own wisdom and spaciousness. We are just one conscious breath away from an awakening or reawakening. Just one conscious breath is all it takes.

Wisdom or natural intelligence which comes from stillness is the other end of the spectrum to knowledge or cleverness. Cleverness is head stuff and is of the ego, and many of us and our public organisations are completely stuck in it. Cleverness feeds off clutter. What the world is crying out for now is less cleverness and more wisdom, discernment, and space. From a point of wisdom, we can start to filter out the constant noise and clutter of all the mental stuff going on in our lives and have the space to reflect.

☾ Let's breathe

Breathing space	The Mantra Breath
Duration	20 minutes, ideally twice a day
Response	To centre my thoughts and awaken my senses
Suited to	Children (the time limit is their age – one minute per year)
Outcome	Faithful knowledge and surrender

Try this now. Take a mantra of your choosing and see how you might syllabicate it. Now play with this and the breath until you find a natural rhythm for you. Make this part of your daily practice and go with it in faith.

Going back to 'Maranatha', it has four syllables: ma·ra·na·tha. Breathe in and sub vocalise 'ma', then breathe out with 'ra'. Breathe in with 'na' and out with 'tha'.

Remember, this is just being offered as an example and a suggestion. Any mantra is deeply personal and so is how you choose to coordinate it with your breath. But don't be heavy about it. Play with it. Have fun and see what works for you.

Breathe, rest in being, and smile.

Chapter 40

The Collective Breath

There is a comfort to crowds of supporters or like-minded people following the same thing.

It is reassuring to be in a group of people with shared interests indicating that they are all collectively right and so, by association, others are wrong. In this way, a duality forms. So much so that the colour of a football jersey creates positive or negative emotions purely on whether it matches yours or not. They make our identity explicit and divide us into visually distinct camps despite all our shared similarities and mutual love of the game.

I was in the terraces recently. The crowd of home supporters went through many different phases. Initially, prior to kick-off, there were greetings and reacquaintances in the community of season ticket holders taking up seats for the match. There is the anticipation of the game and a time to catch up with one another; a time for connection. As the match starts, the competition on the pitch kicks in. The fervour of support for our team is matched with a hostility towards the opposition and vice versa. Identities are clearly divided and established. Geographically we are segregated, and it's clear who the opponents are.

Through our separate identities, we become extremely partisan. Then if events don't go our way, an energy of suspicion and victimisation can develop and escalates in the communicated half-truths and misunderstandings of what is unfolding on the pitch. This becomes very hard to reason against, even in our own head as we become swept up in the tide of emotion. If a decision appears to go the wrong way, there must be a scapegoat and the finger pointed. Nine times out of ten this is the referee – that flawed authority figure – and chants of 'the referee's a bastard' ring around the terraces. Eventually, these choruses build, and momentum and energy attach to it. As the energy coarsens and the anger of the crowd increases, the level of consciousness starts to drop. It is all downhill from here and it spirals on as the game progresses. The referee becomes victimised and scapegoated. The home crowd must be right, so the other lot are wrong. Everyone gets caught in an emotional contagion, at which point we are each so collectively right, come what may, that there is simply no way back to reason.

How could it be any other way? It stands to reason just how right we are because we are all in the same area of the ground, wearing the same jerseys, shouting the same thing, and following the same team with the same intention. Surrounded by so much reinforcement of our position, we become stuck in it. There is no way out. At this point, it takes a huge force of will to say, 'Well that looked like a foul to me, I think it has been called.' As the level of consciousness of the crowd declines it becomes harder to resist.

This is collective ego at play. People are convinced of their own perspective because of communal binds. These binds confirmed by the power of association mean one side is right and that makes the other one wrong. We become entrenched in duality. The collective ego is a very powerful force of unconsciousness – this was just a football match, and we were having a day out supporting our team; imagine if our identification was darker and the stakes were much higher. It literally could lead to war.

Maybe the attraction for us in large groups of people is that by identifying and aligning ourselves with the voice in the crowd, it inoculates us from the need to hear our own voice and sort our own stuff out. There is an unconscious assumption that there is safety in numbers because once all our group identification and collective emotion is gone, we stand alone and need to get on with dealing with our own isolation and pain.

The flaw of many crowds is this descent into negative collective ego. Despite the warmth of the football crowd prior to kick-off, we were drawn there as the game got more heated.

If groups are held by frequency holders, do not focus on the other, and have an intention to be positive, negative collective energy can be avoided. In the concert hall earlier, where people collected in the silence of the moment, there was a sense of unity. I have experienced this as a member of a meditation group for many years. We gathered in silence. Sat together and listened to a talk, then rather than respond, we spent thirty minutes in meditation. At the end of this the group exchanged greetings and left. Although verbal interactions were few, the connections were deep.

The possibilities of coming together are on a spectrum from negative collective ego at one end to community at the other. A group's potential stems entirely from the honest and conscious intention from the outset, or prior to kick-off. Just taking a few conscious breaths connects us to our true being. It raises our consciousness in the moment and helps to clarify intentions. We become more positive yet will probably remain powerless to stop what is going on around us in a large group – but we will see the dynamics at play and hold the big picture more clearly. We may even then be able to remove ourselves or by being there reduce the heat for those around us.

What if we took care of our consciousness the way we do our physical health? Right action of individuals would build and momentum would gather, creating more of it from moment to moment. We would build consciousness, or love, through a *right action chain reaction*.

The weight of numbers within a group and the primal power of negative emotions means that the tendency is to slide towards unconsciousness. The hope is that over time, as more and more people awaken, a true harmonious group may collectively awaken and lead the way. Just before he died, Thich Nhat Hahn said that the next Buddha may not be a person; it may be a sangha, a community.

◯ Let's breathe

Breathing space	Standing In Each Other's Shoes
Duration	Two minutes
Response	To see beyond the surface differences we create
Suited to	Opposing groups
Outcome	Greater empathy

Think of when you have been in a large group. Perhaps at a match when there were other groups of people.

Plant your feet and stand your ground. This tells your mind you are going nowhere and grounds you. Take a conscious breath to see what you are feeling now. Set the intention that you want to see your own truth within the group. Now take three more conscious breaths. Let this settle and process like the glass of cloudy water earlier.

Now look out of your crowd to another one. Cast yourself into that group. Stand in their shoes. Take a conscious breath. Set the intention that you want to see your truth within that group. Now take three more conscious breaths. Let this settle.

Breathe, rest in being, and smile.

Chapter 41

Exploring Unity

'All roads lead to unity because we are already there. There is nowhere to go. The way to walk the path is to know we have already arrived. There is nowhere to go but to be here now.'

– Eknath Easwaran

There is unity in community. Unity is our destiny.

Both to be one with each other in a group and to experience that sense of oneness with our source. All spiritual paths lead to unity. The way to walk our Camino is to know we have already arrived. The pilgrim and the path are one. There is nowhere to go but to be here now.

Being free is seeing things clearly, holding that with compassion, and going from there. It comes from our heart. We come to see that we are both apart yet a part of the whole. Some call this concept of unity 'God', but because God has so many different historical meanings and interpretations, it can be clearer to use more neutral terms like 'universal source energy', 'energetic centre of everything', 'the source of love', or 'unity'.

A definition of unity eludes description because we must explain it through our minds and use words to try to convey something which is well beyond them. More subtly still, in the process of explaining something, we take a step back from it. But we can't step back from something we are. Explaining detaches us from the source of truth and so distances us from its meaning. It's rather like catching a fish so we can ask it about its experience of being wet, or artificially hatching a chick to understand what it is like to be inside an egg. Truth is universal and by searching for it we hide it in plain view.

So, in explaining it we are taking ourselves away from it. Unity is not outside or inside. It is both, and it is everything we can and can't see besides. Unity transcends everything that is. Trying to explain detaches us from it and makes us grasp. In that grasping, we hang on, and by hanging on, all ease and deeper essence is lost.

As we understand ourselves more, we deepen our inner journey and are more able to express the truth from an uncluttered mind. But the problem remains: even from this place we are still using words to express something that is infinitely beyond their capacity. We really hit the buffers trying to explain no-mind with the mind, and are perhaps wisest to stay in silence like the Buddha in the Lotus Sermon. Ultimately this is a path to be breathed and experienced. Words point the way, but they are merely signposts that encourage us to keep travelling the path of experience.

Exposure to the right words and teachings is helpful; most of us slowly surrender to our truth that way. They formed part of my own slippery slope to enlightenment as written about earlier. But words and teaching only get us so far – they are a conceptual ladder of understanding that must be left with gratitude for us to go on and appreciate the rest of the mountain. Krishnamurti says:

> Truth is a pathless land. Man cannot come to it through any organisation, through any creed, through any dogma, priest or ritual, nor through any philosophical knowledge or psychological technique.[28]

Be still. Can you be still? No words. Just breath. Breathe and experience this unity too. It is contained in the resting in being, after the conscious breath. If you find it, smile in gratitude. If you don't, be grateful for the process.

I was walking with old running friends recently. We catch up once a year, and on this occasion, we took a short cut through a graveyard where we stumbled upon the tombstone of Sinead O'Connor, the late great Irish singer who passed in 2023. On it were inscribed just three words in English alongside 'Allah is the greatest' in Arabic. Those three words were: 'God is love.'

◖ Let's breathe

Breathing space	Unity Breath
Duration	One minute
Response	That we are held together by breath
Best for	Deepening our understanding within groups
Outcome	A greater sense of inclusion

We all breathe from the same bubble of air. When we are indoors, this sensation is contained and easier to comprehend. Take a conscious breath.

With the rest in being after the one conscious breath, look around the room. Know that you are all sharing the same room of air. This silent sharing is the invisible breaking of bread. Realise that the air in the room will be inhaled and exhaled by you all. Think of the silent chain of sharing that has gone on.

Now with this awareness, set the intention that you wish to be open to a deepening of the connections between you all. This unity is our destiny. It is travelling in the opposite direction to the concepts of isolation and separation fostered by identification with our ego.

Take a deep breath and a deep sigh. Let go to the truth you have uncovered.

Breathe, rest in being, and smile.

Chapter 42

Let It Go

Parents of seventeen- to twenty-year-old girls are probably still a bit traumatised by the lyrics to the signature song from the movie *Frozen*.

This incredibly successful animation on embracing what lies at our core got played on continuous loop in so many homes shortly after its release date in 2013. I remember running with a friend who told me he had to get out of the house as he had heard the song 'Let It Go' over thirty times that day. Literally. For a joke I recently rang him for the lyrics. Even better, he sang the familiar words over the phone to me.

The only potential problem on the horizon for the distributors was that when we are free, we thaw out to all our clutter and stuff. We become 'un-Frozen'.

Once our mind is free and clear it can be resolved and reconciled to following the wisdom of our heart. Irrespective of fear blocking storms in our minds, we are going to do it. Our heart knows it to be true. We are free and we have set ourselves. *Ready*.

From a clear uncluttered mind, the body gets a clear uncluttered and courageous signal from the heart. It can now fully relax as it is no longer at the beck and call of an untrained mind. The interaction of

211

the untrained mind with the body can be likened to a feral guard dog that is continuously triggered by everything and anyone that passes. In reacting and barking violently in this way, it tugs at its chain, choking and tensing its whole body in sheer frustration at all that comes and goes. That poor guard dog could not be less free.

Instead of the guard dog harming itself, with the freedom and clarity of the mind, the inner choreography of our body falls into sync. Without false distractions, our body can embody its true nature. This is to be in a state of relaxed attention, no longer having to snap at our lead and act out untrained and unhealthy thought patterns. A surrendered awakening combines awakening (what is) with complete trust in the source of that what is. It is the integration of the clarity of the mind from the fully surrendered acceptance of our heart.

Realisations start to flow from this space as we start to uncover what has been holding us back and freezing us for so long. We start to let it go – and we start to thaw. Some of the issues which kept me frozen were explored earlier.

Rather like love, letting go is an infinite and limitless process. We can always love a little bit more, and we can always let go a little bit more. Then from the perspective of a little bit more, a little bit more is possible, and so on and so on. Our exhale is the pathway of letting go and flowing with love.

We are bountiful. There is no end to our love. We can always let go and let out a little more. Our body never fully exhales. So, when you feel there is no more to give, you find it and let go again. It is only with total trust and a sense of safety that we can let go fully. What holds us back from fully loving and fully letting go is our identification with ego. Just as the ego does not want us to awaken, it does not want us to let go. If it can't have full employment, it certainly isn't going to settle for redundancy!

In surrender we jump from the precipice of ego, and realise that we have always been supported and land safely on the soft earth of home.

◯ Let's breathe

Breathing reflection

Take a conscious breath and ask yourself if there is anything you are struggling to let go off. Make a record of this and bring it to a professional counsellor or breath worker to help you initiate the process of letting go.

Breathe, rest in being, and smile.

Chapter 43

You Are Loved.
You Are Safe.

'Come to the edge,' he said.

'We can't, we're afraid!' they responded.

'Come to the edge,' he said.

'We can't. We will fall!' they responded.

'Come to the edge,' he said.

And so they came.

And he pushed them.

And they flew.

– **Christopher Logue**

Bear with me now.

Let's stretch the boundaries of our imagination: I want you to think of your diaphragm as your parachute which, when you go to the edge, will break your fall and keep you safe.

It is a large fibrous sheet below the rib cage and a little way down the back and front of the body. It has a big function within us and often gets overlooked. It moves to enable the breath by facilitating the mechanics of the inhale and exhale. When we have been breathing consciously for a while, particularly in a breathing pattern of conscious connected breathing, our diaphragm quietly takes over and becomes our silent spacious breathing source, flowing from around the navel. When we are in this space, we have moved from breathing to the experience of being breathed. We have become one with the flow of life. This is the same as in meditation when the mantra drops away and we become the meditation. Here everything is still and silent, and everything flows. Deep within us, the diaphragm is this space. It is the source of our alignment – the place of the breath within the breath. Our diaphragm is our source, our inner parachute, our fibrous sheet.

So come to the edge. You are safe. You will keep breathing and you will be completely supported as you do. You are loved and you are love. So you will land. All will be well and new again. Now again.

Letting go is the ultimate act of trust. To jump out of the back of a plane into nothing takes training and trust and despite this, when the side door opens for the first time, we will be flooded with fear. Our chimp will be in overdrive. We must let go of the fear and trust in the process. Just trust in the parachute and the training. Without safety, the jump into the unknown is impossible. Only when the jump has taken place do we realise how easy it was and that we were supported all along. When we are safe and supported, we can physically and psychologically let go of everything.

Change is growth, but freely accepting it is a leap of faith. To let go of everything is the return journey (later this will be called the cosmic exhale). It is completely counterintuitive and makes no sense. To voluntarily let go of a good thing for the hope of no-thing is mind-boggling.

It's kind of what we do on our death beds. To do this while we are still alive, we must be rooted in being to have the faith to let go of it.

In contrast, letting go from a place of ego is not safety, because in the ego we are not aware of the ground of ourselves and so do not have a secure footing from which to let go. Only when the mind is free can the body be ready to jump.

When in the old phrase 'we feel the fear and do it anyway', we are in a very strong place of both being authentic and fully surrendering. In preparation for my first big trip out of Europe, and out of my comfort zone, my friend and I both decided to get our heads shaved. It was forty years ago and we planned to spend four months in India. Shaving our heads felt like a commitment to our cause. I am not sure what it was – were we two innocent wandering aesthetics on the path to whatever came their way?

The day before our departure I went down to the barber next to the village railway station where the commuters would have hurried haircuts before their commute into London. It felt like a good fit for our travels. As agreed, I asked for everything to be shaved off – I was asked to pick a number: four, three, two or one. I chose one. As close as possible to the scalp. I walked home across the common, newly cropped, smoothing the stalks of hair stubble against the palm of my hand on the way.

Mum was horrified. She couldn't look at me. She ran from room to room – as if I had come home tattooed from head to foot. It was a wonderfully reinforcing overreaction, to a life of prior conformity. A few hours later my friend arrived, equally shorn. My mother was then conflicted by how much his new look suited him, whilst mine remained appalling. In the car to the airport, my sister enjoyed rubbing our heads and telling us we were like a new wave band. This wasn't quite the look we had intended for our adventure of a lifetime.

216

Dad, ever the thoughtful fixer, wrote to one of his customers in Bombay, which was somewhere on our route out of northern India to explain that we would like to avail of his kind offer of hospitality but to warn him that we would arrive with shaved heads. When we got to Bombay nearly two months later, sprouting a new look, we were shown Dad's letter with some considerable laughter and disappointment from our host. We no longer looked like two wandering aesthetics; we had returned to our ground, two young middle-class white English blokes trying to get our heads around India.

Complete surrender comes when we surrender with full awareness from a place of authenticity. It helps to be accompanied by a spiritual teacher or a teacher of presence, therapist, breath worker or counsellor. Anybody who has jumped and understands that they are safely holding space for those on the edge. Their space gives us safety to be. Nothing is projected, and no role is established when we meet someone who contains and embodies the space. From their experience and inner space we are held and inspired to let go. In this sense, a fully supportive and safe relationship is where we are holding space and presence for the other. When we have this, we realise we have everything: all we need is within us, and we are finally free to embrace our freedom and jump.

Having jumped doesn't always mean dramatic external shifts take place for others to see. It can be a slippery slope that only gets noticed by the soul – like choosing to walk, when you could be choosing to fight; like waiting in silence, when you could be choosing to talk; like having an alcohol-free beer; like doing the dishes.

Whenever you feel you are holding on in life, sigh, sigh, sigh, and sigh some more. Then, jump.

◯ Let's breathe

Breathing space	The Parachute Breath
Duration	60 seconds
Response	To awaken the diaphragm
Best for	Brave decisions, moments of definition, and life changes
Outcome	Yes, you can

Take a fully conscious breath. Now let's wake up the diaphragm.

Take a deep breath. Now on the exhale, count to ten out loud. Do this as many times as you can on the one exhale. Repeat three times, taking a rest breath between each round.

After a little while, ask, 'How am I breathing now?' Can you now see how you have held onto something recently which is holding you back? It might be in work, friends, family or your home life. Just let go. Then when you let go, let go, let go, and let go. Let go and get yourself un-Frozen. For each letting go, sigh. *Sigh, sigh, sigh and sigh.* Remember, in the section on breath onomatopoeia, the sigh is the sound of letting go.

Let go, let go, let go. You will keep breathing, and your diaphragm will support you. Let go. All will be well as all flows from your deepest core. Let go. You are safe. You are loved.

Breathe, rest in being, and smile.

Part 4

The Cosmic Breath

Just one conscious breath has slowly evolved by adding a smile of gratitude and a sigh of surrender. Now we are entering the deepest level with the deepest breath. This is prompted with a question to assess how we are breathing now – to reveal how we are feeling now – then we add multiple sighs to access the deepest possible levels of letting go.

All this prompts an uncovering of the cosmic breath. Taking this one cosmic breath, our journey comes full circle, and we return to ourselves in a new way – we have taken the curriculum and returned to the dishes.

The complete breath of awakening and surrender, this cosmic breath is:

How am I breathing now? Breathe. Rest in being. Smile. Sigh.

Sigh , sigh, sigh, and sigh some more.

Chapter 44

Coming Home With
One Conscious Breath

*Continue with just one conscious breath by consciously
opening on the inhale and letting go on the exhale.*

Through this, we experientially and incrementally open to our truth.
In the exhale of it all, we learn to let go of everything and just jump.
On the other side of the jump, we know the link between self and
source.

In Chapter 41 we stumbled on the gravestone of Sinead O'Connor.
and the inscription 'God is Love'. Which is the ultimate answer. But
during our lifetimes we have to find our way, which is to become a
unique and authentic expression of that love. We awaken to the
knowledge that *God is love – as I am.*

If God's love is compared to the sun, then ours is like the ray that
touches earth. We ground and embody God's love and are all unique
and authentic expressions of love radiating from source. Our job during

our lives is to be unique and authentic expressions of that love. We are all love, we are all united in love, yet we are different expressions of it.

Glenda Green writes:

> The soul is crying out for a reality experience which only physical life can give it. The body is crying out for an immortality experience which only the soul can give it. As you permit this union to fulfil itself, you will directly know what it feels like to be the love that you are.[29]

Think of our soul as God's yearning within us. Our role is to be unique expressions of love so that God can experience the physical world through us. This is the reality experience of the soul. During our lifetime, our primary job is to find our way, which is the immortality experience that the body is crying out for. Knowing this, we know that we are an expression of love and God is its source.

When we get to this awareness with the breath, it is the cosmic breath. As we inhale, we fill ourselves up with energy – we know that we are, and that we are love – and as we exhale we let go of all identity and surrender into the source of that love.

Knowing this we are free, everything is out of the way, and nature can flow as nature intends. We have awakened with one cycle of the breath. Flowing from the space of our one cosmic breath is our life destiny, and in the words of Ram Dass, is the curriculum.[30] We have fulfilled our life purpose with just one conscious breath.

Each of us must find our own way. It is the path less travelled. There are signposts from those who have gone before, but the surrendered second half of this journey, the place from where we flow, like the *Way* of the Tao, cannot be taken as there is no path to take.

Whilst a desire to know the source of this experience of God is inevitable, this can get in the way. We need to be free. Ultimately this means free of all desires and attachments. Even a heartfelt desire for God is a kind of attachment. It is a form of grasping. Simply trust in it and let go of it.

For the Buddhist, awakening in this way with the breath may be sudden and direct like the smack from a Zen monk referred to earlier, or it can be hesitant and incremental, a bit more like my apologetic slippery slope. When it is incremental, which it probably is for most of us, the cosmic breath builds on all the other breaths that have gone before. Each breath eroding away at our stone of misunderstanding. Then as we start to get it, the breath of awakening is quietly and undramatically breathed. We know it and hear it internally. Life as we knew it slips away and we are quietly renewed.

There is one mountain but many paths. Irrespective of our route the destination is universal. In getting to the summit, we reach our heart. And getting there love becomes our way. We know the love that we are and let life flow from there.

☾ Let's breathe

Breathing reflection

We breathe around thirty thousand times a day – ten million breaths a year – up to a billion in a lifetime. But it just takes one. With a billion attempts, when you breathe consciously with intention, the odds are stacked in your favour. So, the chances of us taking a cosmic breath are high, and when the ground is ready and the time is right, it will happen. Love the process and stay faithful. This is nothing complicated or out of reach.

Your breath is such a loyal companion. Sometimes we are aware of it, sometimes not, but it still flows regardless. It is unconditional and never lets us down from our first moment to our last. In many ways it leads us and guides us and releases us in our final moments. Still quietly teaching us to the very end. And remember, it just takes one. One breath is the membrane between us and an awakening.

Set your desire deep within your heart that you want to know of this breath. Maybe ask one more time then let it fall away. Don't persist – that makes you grasp, and it turns into a nag.

All will be uncovered in breath-time.

Breathe, rest in being, smile, and sigh.

Chapter 45

Life on the Other Side
of the Cosmic Breath

After breathing the cosmic breath, what next?

In his book, *After the Ecstasy, the Laundry*, Jack Kornfield interviews and reflects on people who are said to have reached a state of enlightenment. He finds that their experience of enlightenment comes and goes, and once reached, life and the laundry continue as before. In this way, there is no permanent state of enlightenment. We can't take anything for granted and need to keep working or, more accurately, flowing at it. Rather than being a state of awareness, it is more like there are enlightened actions which are informed from an awakened heart.

So the Zen monks were right: we return to the dishes or the laundry, albeit in a new way. The new way is to be fully present in the moment of the dishes. We now know that the dishes are enough, and everything is contained in the present moment of doing them. As we quietly breathe and experience our being on the inside, we may directly experience the feel, the softness of the water, the scrape of the dishes, the bubbles rise and pop. We do the dishes in a fully mindful way.

The limitation in trying to understand ourselves is that we only have ourselves to do it with; as in Chapter 36, we are our own problem. Here we have the equivalent of a Zen koan (riddle) of awakening: 'How do you experience emptiness through content?' Emptiness is our core but all the stuff and ways of looking for it are the clutter of content. What we are looking for is there but it is not possible to see and understand with what we have, and the moment we come close to it and conceptualise it, we create a false distance between us and it. This is why it is so hard to write or talk about as it is beyond our capacity, and it is why the Buddha held the lotus flower in the air in the silent sermon.

It's only when we turn off the conceptual mind, let everything be and let it all pass, that we discover it was there all along, in our heart. The only way is no way, to let go and let be. Fully surrender everything you know and hold dear. So, drop the hot stone, drop the bag, drop your being, and drop the breath. Drop it all. Let go and let it all be.

In the famous saying, we 'let go and let God' in the glorious exhale of it all. This journey to being, and beyond to surrender, is who we are. It is our life; the other side of what we had previously thought it was. This is the only journey we really must make. It is the path from an overcrowded head to a spacious loving heart.

By consciously bringing the cosmic inhale and exhale together, we are whole – we are. We have breathed the entire curriculum of awakening and beyond. We have found our heart and know that it is love and that it is energetically connected to the love of the universe. Everything is contained in this one cosmic breath. We reside there now in our heart and experience a sense of union, however fleetingly. Nothing else really matters in comparison.

Let's return briefly to our seat in the National Concert Hall, inspiration comes from all angles. Having breathed the entire curriculum in one breath, the knowing we now have is that place of *wow, just wow* when we let go and know that *there is no more.*

◯ Let's breathe

Breathing reflection

Set an intention in your heart to breathe the cosmic breath in breath time.

How am I breathing now? Breathe. Rest in being. Smile. Sigh.

Sigh, sigh, sigh, and sigh some more.

Chapter 46

Awaken.
Breathe. Be.

With awakening, we realise that the state we used to call our life is not our life.

In some traditions this is likened to waking up from a dream and is where the term 'awaken' comes from. We realise that our mind-made egoic states and associated thoughts and feelings that we previously identified with are not us. Just like the raised flower bed written of earlier, they are the sediment that formed the stone of our identity. The stone is so pervasive and so apparently permanent, but it is not who we are – it is just the stuff that surrounds the process of becoming somebody. It formed a wall that disguised our true selves. Our true self is to know the stillness and spaciousness of who we are in our heart. We share this stillness and spaciousness with everyone. It's always there – we just have to lift the stones first.

Our life is not egoic, it is universal, and we all share this one life. In some traditions, transcending the ego is a state called egoic death. For those of us who have travelled to this point slowly, undramatically, and incrementally, this statement feels big and sudden. The ego may continue to have its own cravings. Remember, what we resist persists. If we think that we have extinguished it, it may respond to the challenge and come back at us, one sip at a time. It may be more realistic to live with it. Earlier I wrote that it is a bit like rehoming an endlessly distractable stray puppy. So let's take that ego puppy in. Let's offer it a home, befriend it, enjoy it even, smile at it often – but whatever you do, don't let it demand you keep topping up its bowl. Remember, your heart is the boss of this relationship now.

Your one conscious breath has got you here. So when your ego yaps at you, express your gratitude at one more opportunity to take a conscious breath.

Life is fully lived when we completely let go of everything we previously thought was true. The thoughts we had were not our thoughts. We accepted this narrative from the outside, so there is nobody to blame. It was just like the script of a play. That's okay. We have to realise that there is no script, and we can simply take our place on the universal stage. To fully embrace this life, we must surrender the script of becoming. With our cosmic breath, we have taken the journey of our life and realised it is not what we previously thought it was. We know of being run by ego and have woken up from it. And then we fully surrendered from this space. At this point it is not so much a case of who wakes up but what wakes up within us.

Our awareness of the energy of love within us comes and goes, like an electricity supply in a thunderstorm, but it is never further than one conscious breath away. Having touched the source with the breath, we can return there with it. Consciousness is and is not lost – love is and is not lost. Breathing consciously in this way becomes a portal of remembering of who, or what, we are and enables us to be here, knee deep in the laundry.

We can only experience the truth of the impermanence of everything within us through the lens of what is not. What remains in the impermanence of it all is what we experience it with. This is our consciousness or, more accurately, universal consciousness. It remains completely beyond our ability to define, but we know it is immanent and flows through everything. It is the never-ending energy of love. It is the Tao that we cannot speak of.

○ Let's breathe

Breathing reflection

We are all a unique expression of the one spectrum of light. Our job is to take the curriculum, to wake up to it, or, more accurately, be sufficiently empty for it to wake up in us. Take one conscious breath. How am I breathing now?

Breathe. Rest in being. Smile. And sigh. Sigh, sigh, sigh, and sigh some more.

Chapter 47

Our Re-Entry Into Life

Reading this, you have taken the journey from a clear, uncluttered head to an open and loving heart.

It starts at the head and completes in the heart because only when our mind is free of all the programmes that have been running it for years can the heart fully open and enable us to flow with the universal tide of life. This is flowing with love. Once we are here, we see and claim our birthright which is our capacity for peace and contentment in the present moment. Jack Kornfield calls this the great errand:

> We each have a great errand. In time we must awaken.
> Awakening may hide in our attic for years waiting until
> we raise our children or finish our business careers, but
> some day it will break down the gate and say ready or
> not here I come.[31]

This awakening is a universal yet simultaneously individual calling. We must take our own way. We all face our own challenges, yet the destination remains the same.

We are unique expressions of unity. In the diversity of our lives is the abundance and wholeness of source energy seeking expression for itself through us. We are called to be fully authentic and to be ourselves and if we do not lead our lives in this way, no one else will. Each of us will wake up in a different way to different timetables. To wake up is our destiny and ultimate life purpose. In *Love Without End* by Glenda Green, it says, 'Everyone has a covenant and a purpose which is special, and if you do not fulfil it there is no one else who will.'

So be generous to yourself and to your life. Compassion, particularly self-compassion, is key on the journey. Do everything that you can to nourish and support yourself and when you slip, which happens to me regularly, smile in gratitude for another opportunity to learn and to breathe. Like the action of water on the stone, gentleness and repetition get us there.

Our journey of awakening is then both personal and universal. The sacredness of this and the limitations of words means that sometimes it is wisest not to share. But that is not very encouraging for other people. For me it sort of happened when I felt myself being breathed. For a long time, I was just heart and breath. At this point, I embodied and experienced the lesson I needed. This was very unexpected and became the seed of this book. It happened in a small cabin at the end of a barge on the River Thames in London. The boat was rocking slowly with the movement of the tide and the passing of other boats. I was accompanied by my breath worker and we were in the middle of a conscious connected breathing session. As I looked up I saw the beautiful old planked wooden ceiling of the boat gently rocking with the lapping river. I realised that for some considerable time I had been breathed. The river was flowing beneath me and the river of life was flowing through me. It was all one. For all my travelling and living abroad, it took place on a boat just two miles upstream from where I had been born fifty-five years earlier.

When I consciously breathe I remember and remind myself of that point in time. Just one conscious breath returns me to the sensation of being breathed in gratitude. It makes sense that we all walk through our stuff to reach this essence here now. Irrespective of our backgrounds, complexities, neurotypes and beliefs, we are all destined to wake up. To take one fully cosmic breath. This human journey of ours is at the same time separate yet universal.

Once the cosmic breath has been taken, we return to the dishes. Everything changes and yet nothing does. Our interior life becomes fuller and reflects in all we do, even when the exterior stays the same. The thinking mind has receded, and our days are punctuated with more blue sky. And a breath becomes a pause of reawakening.

After the cosmic breath, we are on the inside looking out and know the difference the breath has made. In the ordinariness of it, we have come full circle and returned to the laundry. But on the way we have uncovered everything. Once we have breathed the cosmic breath, just one conscious breath becomes like a wheel of remembering and return, bringing us back full circle to our breath and our wholeness.

This wheel of remembering can be visualised within the circular image of our jumping dolphin:

How am I breathing now? Breathe. Rest in being. Smile. Sigh. Sigh, sigh, sigh and sigh some more. How am I feeling now?

Remember to surface regularly to breathe.

Chapter 48

The Heavenly Gate

The final tweak to this wheel of breath and remembering and letting go is wherever and whenever we can to breathe through the nose. We can breathe consciously, or we can breathe unconsciously, and by watching ourselves we help to change the habit and the pathway.

Earlier the power of nasal breathing and listening was explained. When we breathe through our nose, we signal to the talker that we are there and attentive and are not about to jump in. Listening attentively is just one aspect of breathing through the nose in the grand scheme of things. Ancient Chinese mystics referred to the nose as the heavenly gate. So much is written about the benefits of nasal breathing over mouth-breathing. We breathe with the nose and eat with the mouth. This is their function, and whilst we can breathe through the mouth (and half the world's population predominantly does), as a long-term habit, it makes about as much sense as adopting the nose to eat with.

If we had an organ in our body which moistened the air we breathe, warmed it in cool environments, cooled it in warm ones, filtered it, and showed evidence of having an antimicrobial role against airborne diseases – then surely we would use it. *Right?* Especially when you think that the alternative is to breathe in all that dry, dirty air at the wrong temperature through our mouths. The truth is literally staring us in the face. To fully access the benefits of one conscious breath, we need to shut our mouths and breathe through the nose. When we nose breathe, we wake up and smell the coffee.

How are you breathing now? As you see yourself mouth-breathing, it is just an invitation to return to nasal breathing. To change to nose breathing. Move on up to the heavenly gate. Build a new habit, one breath at a time. As you are aware of the channel you are breathing through, try and monitor your inner state.

Try and track your feelings with how you are breathing. Become your own laboratory – it is *your* breath, after all. As Krishnamurti states, 'Ultimately the only truth is the one we experience and understand for ourselves.'[32] It is our job to do our own thing and uncover our own truth – mine was most profoundly revealed through conscious connected breathing on the barge and through hours of nose breathing amidst the delays and chaos at the airport.

As we build our own understanding and truth, we can start to extend it outwards – how are other people breathing when they are in different emotional states? What can you do to help? Can you model to them in the same way that we learned to model to the children with autism and complex needs when they were in crisis?

Become your own researcher – don't listen to anyone. You don't need a guru or a teacher. You don't need to follow anyone. All you need to is become a pilgrim of your breath. Do you remember Krishnamurti's quote about truth being a pathless land? So go ahead and ask yourself, 'How am I breathing now?' as often as possible, and move to the heavenly gate. Consciously breathe through your nose. If you find yourself breathing through your mouth, smile in awareness and change. If you're breathing through your nose, smile in gratitude and accept. Ultimately you will find yourself breathing more through your nose.

The end is now in sight, and the one conscious breath has evolved with the process of writing and reflection to become:

How am I breathing now?

Take one conscious breath in and out of the nose.

Rest in being.

Smile. Sigh.

Sigh, sigh, sigh, sigh and sigh

How am I feeling now?

Adding the sighs, the one conscious breath has become several, and through the question, it has also become a reflective practice. In breathing it we have completed the curriculum or performed the great errand which is to breathe one cosmic breath. It has been breathed by combining the energetic inhale of becoming and the surrendered sigh of release.

Our breath is a constant from our first to last day. It will never stop until it is ready. Trust in it. This quiet, loyal, invisible, and undemonstrative companion teaches us everything we need to know.

Taking this fully cosmic breath leads us to our awakening and the freedom on the other side of that. There are other routes to travel there, but having reached blocks on the way in taking them, the breath has become my Camino. Once it has been breathed, life goes on, often unremarkably. But we are our unremarkable selves in the moment. When we slip out of now, we know we can simply take one conscious breath to return there. When we do this our conscious breath returns us to our awakening rather than realising it.

We have come to the end. As fellow pilgrims of breath, we have walked together and breathed together. We have reached our Santiago, but truly, this is only the beginning. Your life, your freedom, your love, your energy, your will to keep on – it all happens on the return home. Take just one conscious breath here now. Then take it out on the road with you. Let your life become a pilgrimage of your breath.

Celebrate the air inside you, the expanse that becomes you. I am here to share with you only this: in breath, you are held; you are loved and you are never alone. And each and every time you choose to breathe consciously, you shall arrive home, as if, perhaps, for the very first time.

You are here.

Appendix

Breath Glossary and Useful Techniques

This final section is split into three: breaths of awakening, breaths of surrender, and breaths of empowerment. Although this book is about the central role of just one conscious breath, in breathing it, we open the awareness and opportunity to learn and practise other breaths.

Breathwork is used as a pillar for spiritual connection and awakening across many religions. Buddha said the road to enlightenment started and ended with the breath. Pranayama, an ancient practice of the breath, is an integral part of yoga. In the West too we have seen the power of the breath, particularly in the community prayers, like saying the rosary, where groups of people kept together in rounds of successive prayer. In the rounds and repetition, religious communities and families became in sync with one another and their breath subsequently became harmonised.

But this is not a book about breathwork. There are many excellent ones available. This is a book about how I have found just one conscious breath to be a spiritual practice and a golden thread through my life, keeping me awake and reminding me of my connection to source energy. This is the highest power of breathwork.

People are reawakening to the power of the breath. Breathwork is becoming widely understood as a very powerful tool and breathwork communities are growing. There are literally millions of different types of breaths we can use to support us, and they broadly fall into the three groups above.

Breathing consciously reminds us that where we are going is here and whatever we do is opening our hearts to what is in front of us. There is nothing to grasp or hang onto because when we do, we act in a way that tells us that we don't already have it – but we do. It is just in the looking that we distance ourselves further from it. In conscious connected breathing we don't hold onto our breath. There is no need to hold on; let it come and let it go smoothly. The moment is now, and the breath flows freely with it. The breath is our gentle, life-sustaining companion and a portal to access what is in front of us right now – every time we return to it consciously, we have that opportunity to awaken or reawaken to this truth.

Breathing is the only bodily system that we can do both unconsciously and consciously. We can't consciously digest our food or circulate our blood, but we can consciously intervene with our breath for a desired end. Breath is the most powerful tool at our disposal to access being and to build a bridge between our head and our heart.

Just one conscious breath is a small tool to use whenever we can, rather like a brain app. It is a way to bring consciousness and remembering into what we do and who we are. With repeated use, it opens the space in us and helps us to see the space in another person. From here we can choose the breath we need most in the moment to support us. The ones I use and find most supportive are explained here.

Breaths of Awakening

Breaths of awakening are the starting point and, when practised regularly with intention and trust, will bring huge results. Trust is important. When we practise in faith and trust, unconcerned with results, we get our egoic needs out of the way and so free up the breath to flow where we need it to go.

Intention is not of the ego. We may say to ourselves something like 'at the end of this session I would like to have a fresh insight into …' Try it with something that is currently disturbing you, and for which a solution seems ungraspable. Earlier in the book, I referred to a friend who always said he would sleep on a problem. This is the same thing. We also had the example of someone throwing the number of books down on the floor to accompany the number of questions to be resolved. This too is the same thing. Both these are not of the ego that needs to solve and control a situation. In both examples the unconscious mind is being kindly invited to respond to an open question.

In taking breaths of awakening, we aim to engage our parasympathetic nervous system so we can ease into a place of calm and peace. The first two recommended breaths follow exercise. Sustained and systematic exercise brings us to calm and fuller, deeper breaths – this is a wonderful jumping-off point into an exploration of breath.

1. Cardiovascular Exercise

A key breath of awakening is simply to watch our breath after exercise. Motion and emotion are linked and when we move, we feel better. After an extended period of running, vigorous walking, or cycling, we reach a wonderful state where our heart rate has been elevated for a sustained period. The US Department of Health recommends raising the heart rate five times a week for thirty minutes, for a total of at least 150 minutes each week, for our long-term health.[33]

After cardiovascular exercise we naturally breathe deeper into the bottom of the lungs. This is where most of the nerves that support the parasympathetic nervous system are. Cardiovascular exercise provides the double whammy of the buzz of exercise from a sustained elevated heart rate with the relaxation given by longer deeper breaths. This is the holy grail of relaxed alertness talked about throughout the exploration of one conscious breath, and is why exercise really is the best medicine.

Some organisations, particularly those where colleagues are more desk-bound, are integrating total wellness programmes into the workday to overcome the go-to refrain of 'I don't have time to exercise.' Not only do these groups give access to the physical benefits of regular exercise, they provide an opportunity to make connections with colleagues and reduce stress.

When you are experiencing longer, deeper breaths after exercise, try and double up on them by inhaling and exhaling through the nose. This is also a good time to start a breath awareness practice. You are naturally breathing deeper and slower after exercise. So, look at it and understand it, ideally when lying down. From this place start to experience the journey of the breath. In this way, you may feel:

· the tingle of air as it ripples the entrance of your nostrils,
· the passage of air as it moves on up through the nose,
· your upper chest as it fills with air,
· how this deepens down to your belly, and
· how your belly rises and falls on the tide of breath.
·

Watch the return as you exhale all the way through to the subtle, almost imperceptible sensation at the tip of your nostrils as the breath leaves. When we look at something that we do unconsciously, we bring consciousness to it. Take time after cardiovascular exercise to explore the breath; it is a wonderful opening into the world of breathwork.

2. Swim the Front Crawl

In swimming the front crawl, or freestyle as you may know it, a few great breathing disciplines are forced on us. We have to:

· adapt to a new environment,
· use the mouth for the inhale to avoid lungfuls of water,
· consciously change the channel of breathing to exhale underwater through the nose,
· in so doing remember this is our heavenly gate,

- inhale and exhale to a regular count, and
- coordinate breath and movement.

Swimming is the ultimate exercise, not just because it gives us a whole-body workout but also because it is load-bearing and we are fully supported by the water. We also get to coordinate movement and breath. In front crawl especially there is no way we can fake it because our head is underwater half the time. It is a kind of joint pranayama and yoga practice.

We get all the benefits of a cardiovascular workout with the coordination of a systematic breathing pattern. The breath is coordinated with the number of arm movements, or strokes, taken. An odd number of strokes is recommended for balance as each time we inhale is on the opposite side. So it goes:

- lean to one side,
- inhale through the mouth,
- hold,
- exhale underwater through the nose for three or five strokes,
- lean to the other side, and
- breathe through the mouth again.
·

Swimming in open water is particularly beneficial. In doing the front crawl we are systematically doing the breath. It is a very short step from swimming the front crawl to practising rounds of Box Breathing.

3. One Hundred Conscious Breaths

Just one conscious breath is enough, but more are better. A period of twenty minutes of reflection, twice a day, is recommended for anyone who wishes to build a practice. I have approximated this to one hundred slow, conscious breaths.

The problem with giving a number is it can become an obstacle. Don't try and recall where you are, as that turns the head back on and defeats the purpose. Set a timer or play a piece of reflective instrumental music for twenty minutes or so, then breathe in and out slowly through your nose.

We all get distracted. At these times, know that's just the jibber-jabber trying to get back in. Attach no value to it. It's just the eternal junk mail of the mind (but don't label it as it then becomes a thought, and bingo – they're back). Watch the breath come and go, like clouds passing across the sky or soap bubbles rising slowly before popping. In a way, be grateful for distractions because every time we are distracted, it is one more opportunity for return and renewal.

There is no difference between good and bad thoughts. They are all clouds, so just let them go. They are absolutely of no value and will present themselves in the most suitable way to distract you at any given time. It's like they know your weak spot. It is a constant dance between being and thought. For most of us, it is only with time and practice that the dynamic starts to change. We get glimpses of being then can slip back into thought, until one conscious breath, like an internal temple chime, brings us back to ourselves. Don't grasp or set targets. Very few people can be in a constant state of no thought, and they include some of the enlightened masters that have been written about here.

4. Breath of Body Awareness

We have brought a period of awareness into the one conscious breath by asking 'How am I breathing now?' Knowing how we are breathing will reveal how we are feeling.

A deeper exploration of breath awareness is the breath of body awareness. This is linked to the famous yoga nidra session where following a period of movement, different parts of the body are relaxed, one by one. This time though, we are going to use the breath to bring awareness to different parts of the body and then back again for integration.

Create a time of retreat for yourself. Find a place of calm and set aside ten to fifteen minutes. Turn off your phone and any other distractions. Play some instrumental, uncluttered music if you wish – solo guitar, piano, or cello works well, but anything that doesn't stimulate thought is fine. Close your eyes gently. Sit in a chair with your spine straight – you can use a wedge or small pillow propped under the tailbone to help. Rest the palms of your hands face up or face down on your knees. Breathe in through the nose and feel the air pass the entrance to your nostrils and the small sensation of vibration this can create. Centre yourself with a few rounds of this breath.

Bring your attention slowly and systematically from the outer to the inner. Breathe into the furthest sound you can hear, then slowly trace the sounds back to you in a funnelled web of attention. Can you hear sounds outside the room, then within the room, the music playing, and now the sounds of the air as it gently vibrates your nostrils passing through?

Ask yourself a question now with your hands resting still on your knees: How do I even know I have hands? This internalises attention within the body.

Now with the inhale bring the air lower and slower down into the belly. Do some deep abdominal breaths. Feel the air fill the belly to the front, then around the sides and the back. Slowly exhale through the nose. Do a few rounds of this.

We are now going to use the breath to acknowledge different parts of the body by touching and releasing them. Slowly breathe into your forehead with the inhale and release with the exhale. We will move with the breath from head to toe and back again. Bring your attention to:
· your eyebrows,
· the gap between your eyebrows,
· the backs of your eyes,
· your eyelids,

- your lips,
- your teeth,
- your cheeks,
- your chin,
- your throat,
- your shoulders,
- your elbows,
- your hands,
- your chest,
- your belly button,
- a place an inch or so below your belly button,
- your sit bones,
- your thighs,
- your knees,
- the soles of your feet,
- your heels, and
- your toes.

Now back up again:
- ankles,
- knees,
- sit bones,
- base of the spine,
- lower spine,
- middle of the spine,
- upper spine,
- lower jaw,
- upper jaw,
- nose,
- eyebrows, and
- the space between the eyebrows.

Continue to breathe into the space between the eyebrows for a while. Now start to turn your attention to the outer. Can you hear the following sounds? The passage of air across your nostrils, the music playing quietly, sounds of the room, sounds outside the room, and now sounds outside the house? Breathe into the furthest sound you can hear and open your eyes. Watch how you are breathing now.

5. Belly Breathing

The majority of the nerves that support the parasympathetic nervous system are low down in the belly. The diaphragm has been likened to our parachute of safety that keeps us breathing when everything else drops away. It is the source of these abdominal breaths. The silent space that quietly takes over in the deepest times when we have the experience of being breathed. This is where we are trying to go with the next breath. We are trying to access deep, conscious abdominal breaths.

Play some instrumental music if you wish. Lie on your back in a quiet, undisturbed space. Have your palms facing down, resting a little way out from the body in a way that is supportive and comfortable. There is no need for special equipment, but if you wish you can place a small, rolled towel under the bottom of your spine and have your knees bent so a steep triangle is formed.

Now awaken the diaphragm: Breathe in a deep breath, slowly through your nose. Open your lips, and on the exhale count quickly from one to ten.

One-two-three-four-five-six-seven-eight-nine-ten. Repeat. Try and repeat this for five, six, or seven rounds before you need another inhale. Take that inhale naturally. Then go again for two more rounds of this. This prepares the diaphragm for what will happen next.

Close your eyes. Breathing through your nose, watch your belly fill with air from the front, sides, and back. Be aware of your belly button and visualise it rising and falling. Just let the air out quickly. The mouth is good for this as it is bigger. Hear a kind of exaggerated sigh as you do this. Breathe continuously in this way and keep your awareness on your belly as it rises and falls. Stay in this space for about one hundred breaths. Become aware of the spaciousness created by your abdomen and let go. Keep letting go. Let go of all attention and allow that silent spacious breathing source to take over and to breathe you. Let go of your awareness of that.

Be in the silent spaciousness created by your breath.

Slowly, return attention to the sounds of the room. Open your eyes and take time to come back to your physical self. This is also a beautiful breath of being and of surrender and is one of the key breaths to practise when developing a holistic wellness and awareness breath practice.

6. Mind the Gap Breath

The gap created by taking one conscious breath is the spaciousness that naturally happens within and around us after breathing it. This has also been referred to as the *wisdom gap*. There are momentous gaps too in nature. The turning of the tide is a special time when the currents are still or not stressed and it becomes safer for divers. This can be on the low ebb tide or the high slack tide. A beach pebble picked up at low tide and thrown directly in the air will keep rising with the momentum of the throw, then start to slow down until it imperceptibly pauses on the ascent at a point where there is no energy behind it, and then turns to slowly fall and accelerates with the force of gravity. If the stone were the sun, the pause at the top is like the summer equinox – a time of huge spiritual significance for millennia and celebrated at Stonehenge. Minding the gap is a special time in nature and for us.

Just like the tide and the pebble, we have two natural movements. The rising tide corresponds to the inhale and the falling tide is the exhale. And just like the tide, our breath has a period of stillness and rest before the return movement. These are the almost imperceptible pauses of turn and return that happen when the inhale flows into the exhale and the exhale flows into the inhale.

When these pauses become conscious, they can become breath holds, which are very powerful in breathwork. In breaths of awakening, we use these pauses as natural portals into the present moment by feeling and exploring the turn of our own tide. This is not achieved by holding the breath but simply by bringing awareness to the turn and sense of the stillness and spaciousness that naturally happens here.

When we become available to the stillness and spaciousness in our breath and start to feel it and understand it, we open to the stillness and spaciousness within us. When we know this, we have awoken from an earlier identification with our false self. We are accessing being and breathing the cosmic inhale.

Sit or lie down quietly, prepare, and after a period of conscious breathing, start to watch your breath. As you watch it, become aware of the physical sensation of the turning of the tide within you. Explore very briefly what that feels like, and with each turn of the breath, bring your consciousness to the space within you. As you feel this space, you can let go. Just let it be and feel your inner spaciousness. From this point you are no longer consciously breathing; at a deeper level still, you are being breathed.

Over time, the tide of this breath points the way and surrenders to the flow of life.

Breaths of Surrender

The energetic cycle of the breath is the inhale. This corresponds to the outer phase of our life when we become somebody through the life process of 'I' accumulation. When we transcend that and reach our inner stillness and spaciousness, we are in a state of being and non-thinking, however temporarily.

Having woken up to who or what we are with the breath, the next stage is to let go of it all and just let it all be. This corresponds with the exhale where we physically let go of the breath. We can only fully surrender from a place of awareness, where the egoic mind has been recognised and transcended.

In terms of the spiritual power of the breath, the exhale, the phase of surrender is the most powerful one. With the exhale, we drift on the thermals of the flow of life and are open and available to what comes our way.

Also by emptying ourselves of everything, we are readying to open up more and more to the flow of life. When we let go and open ourselves up to the possibility of getting lost, a way is found. This is the unsignposted way of the Tao.

The breaths of surrender that follow are linked to the exhale and are primarily about letting go.

7. Surface and Exhale with a Dolphin Breath

Having been an intention from the outset and our companion throughout, *our dolphin breath finally surfaces.*

Taking a conscious breath is a bit like becoming a dolphin. Like us, a dolphin has lungs, and a blowhole for a nose, which is sealed when underwater. But unlike us, the dolphin can't unconsciously breathe. They physically surface every eight minutes to come up for air. That's what I am inviting you to do.

 Become a land dolphin.

Pause and take a conscious breath. As you read this book, or better still swam through it, there were opportunities through breathing spaces and reflections to consciously breathe and come up for air every few minutes. Turn this into a regular practice whenever you can – become a land dolphin. When one conscious breath is practised repeatedly and with increased awareness, our inner truth will slowly be uncovered. Then with continued faith in the practice of conscious breathing, we are led to a place of surrender where everything is held.

Surface and exhale.

Each breathing space is a new opportunity to experience and embody the writing through the breath. The more we introduce conscious breaths to our life the better. You may consciously breathe at the end of each paragraph, or between sentences.

 Become a land dolphin.

As you start on this path of conscious breathing, become like a land dolphin swimming through your life. Surface every eight minutes or so to take a conscious breath. At first you may enable this by using prompts or technology to remind you.

 Surface and exhale.

8. Conscious Connected Breathing

Leonard Orr is the founder of this type of breathwork. It goes by different names: conscious connected breathing, circular breathing, rebirthing, rebirth breathwork, intuitive energy breathing, and source breathwork. It was developed by him in the early sixties while taking a bath. He found that he could relax more deeply by taking rounds of successive breaths without any pause. Initially, with the first trainees in California, this was done in warm water, with snorkels and nose clips.

The majority of transformational breathwork trainings focus on this when teaching the power of breath. This is what I wrote about when describing the experience of being breathed on the barge. Because of its transformational nature, it is the most widely used breath of spiritual awakening by breath workers.

This is the alchemist's breath, but because of the power it touches off, and what it brings up, it must be supervised by a qualified breath worker who puts your safety first. This breathing is practised for a sustained period of forty-five minutes or so. The air is inhaled in and out of the mouth through a relaxed throat. The mouth is preferred because it is a bigger opening and so more efficient for this type of breathwork. The emphasis is on the exhale. We are accompanied by a trainer who encourages us to fully let go. Sometimes we let go of the exhale quickly, so unnecessary energy is not spent on the release.

The breath is circular in nature with the completion of the inhale seamlessly merging with the initiation of the exhale and vice versa. There are no gaps, as in some other breaths, and we bring no awareness to these points. When there are no gaps, there is no resistance, and flow happens. The breath symbolises the merging of the opposite forces within us – on and off, Yin and Yang, male and female. Each session lasts about 1½ hours – bookended by spiritual accompaniment.

The pace may be suggested by the breath worker, and if there is any resistance, sometimes faster-than-normal breathing may be used. It is an extremely powerful technique, and when undertaken in the presence of an awakened and trained breath therapist over a series of ten sessions or so, it is transformational. In doing this, a lot of emotional issues come up.

For me, after about eight 1½ to 2-hour sessions, the penny dropped. Just eight sessions of this breathing technique with a world-renowned breath worker taught me what thirty years of meditation and countless other interventions hadn't. I knew the need to let go and see the psychological and egoic blocks I had put in the way of this happening.

The breath worker is key as the client can initially only be supported as deeply as the breath worker has gone previously. The space within the breath worker holds the space for the client and allows the client's breath to do the work for them. So we do the breath, and the breath does us. It is a deeply healing and transformational process.

Once people have completed this, a period of just twenty connected breaths twice daily or so can remind us of this surrendered state. The wonderful thing is our consciousness, unlike physical fitness, never goes away, but like fitness, regular practice is best.

9. Loosening the Temporomandibular (TM) Joint

A crocodile has such a powerful downward jaw muscle that it can snap an animal in half, yet it cannot open its jaws to overcome a strong rubber band wrapped around its snout. We have very strong jaw muscles too. Pound for pound it is by far the most powerful muscle in our body. It is called the temporomandibular (or TM) joint and it connects our lower jaw to the skull. It gives power to the bite and lateral movement of the mouth. When people are stressed, their TM muscles can sometimes be seen pulsating at the back of the jaw. When you hear someone say that they did something 'through gritted teeth', you can visualise the stress it was causing them by looking here.

This breath releases the TM joint and is an overall de-stressor and source of surrender.

The first phase is to loosen out the TM joint. Lie on your back with your palms face up. Place a towel in the small of your back and have your knees bent if you wish. For a minute or two, loosen your jaw by moving it from side to side and bring your chin forward and back as if trying to catch a drop of falling rain from the sky.

Now, breathe in through the nose and breathe out with a big, exaggerated sigh of release. Do this at least twenty times.

Return to your TM joint and quickly repeat the above exercise. Now, while still on your back, breathe in through your nose and yawn. Do this twenty times or so.

Next the sigh and yawn of release are going to be combined on the exhale. Breathe in through the nose. Start a wonderful big, exaggerated yawn, and halfway through the exhale, switch it over to a sigh of release.

Check in with your TM joint for a final time.

10. Lengthen the Exhale

The exhale is the breath of letting go. Try to consciously lengthen it. A ratio of 1:2 works well. So, breathe in for a count of four, then turn the breath around to an exhale of eight. Other lengths work too, but keep the ratio at 1:2.

One way to lengthen the inhale and the exhale is to regulate the flow of the breath in and out of the lungs. There is a pranayama technique written about earlier called ujjayi breathing. This is sometimes called the ocean breath because the passage of air through the throat can make an internal sound reminiscent of the rising and falling tide. To do this, close the mouth and put the tongue to the start of the soft palate on the roof of your mouth. Inhale and exhale through this space and the constricted throat will make the ocean sound. The breath can be controlled and slowed in this way, and it is a very good technique for consciously intervening in the breath.

When your body hears a long exhale, it is an audible invitation for it to relax. This happens with ujjayi breathing. With the slow, steady passage of air, the body senses that there is nothing to worry about; everything is under control. The body picks up the signal and lets go a little more. With this a reinforcing virtuous cycle has been created.

11. Sigh Consciously

The greatest primal fear that we have is not being able to breathe. So, when you are feeling stressed, take just one conscious breath and ask yourself, can I take the next breath? Knowing we can contextualises our stress and dampens it down.

If you find yourself stressed, just sigh frequently. Sigh in the car, sigh in the shopping aisles, sigh in the queue, sigh in traffic, sigh on the train, sigh at work. *Sigh, sigh, sigh and sigh some more.* When you are in a situation where you are feeling provoked and don't want to respond, just sigh and keep sighing. This is how we modelled relaxation to the children at school who were not available to hear us because they were in crisis.

The ujjayi breath can be used when it is not appropriate to sigh out loud. Using this we can always have a long internal silent sigh. Our ujjayi breath makes a different sound on both the inhale and exhale. Try it and hear that now. On the inhale is a reassuring sound, like a kind of big breath syringe, gently pulling up air. On the exhale, it reverses; you can hear the plunger slowly pushing out the air, rather like a subvocalised sigh. This sound of release is a more socially acceptable, slow, silent surrendered sigh and can be performed when dramatic and multiple sighing is not possible. This was the technique I used when driving in the car on the motorway in driving rain and tailbacks.

Far from being inattentive or a signal of boredom, sighing and yawning are clear signs of our bodies' needs. We can consciously develop a practice that includes them, and when we feel one coming on, recognise it in gratitude and jump on it.

12. Cold Water Swimming Breaths

In Dublin, during Covid we were restricted to a two-kilometre walk from our house. Like spiders on an invisible thread, we explored our web in depth like never before. Two kilometres got us into the local village and down to the sea. The sea there is tidal and grey and very unappetising. All the nice places to swim are a few kilometres away down the coast and outside of the web, but needs must. I had never explored the possibility of swimming there prior to Covid because, quite frankly, why would you? The sea is on the wrong side of the train tracks, and we must cross over the concrete railway bridge to come to a patch of weeds running alongside the wire mesh protecting us from the railway line. The other side of the weeds is the graffiti and concrete of a wall separating the railway line and everyone else from the high seas. A break in the wall leads to more concrete and a platform beyond to the sea. At the end of the platform, there are a few concrete steps and an antiquated, corroded and wobbly handrail offering some support. It became our heaven.

A socially distanced and eclectic group of us came together on WhatsApp and a supportive, dedicated cohort was born. Besides, there was little else happening at the time and the lure of a warm post-swim takeaway coffee from one of the few outlets allowed to trade their way through the pandemic sealed the deal. A couple of years on we are still swimming on the wrong side of the tracks and a life ring has appeared.

Cold water swimming is good for mental health,[34] which overcomes the restricted exercise benefits that a quick lunge into the icy green winter water provides. Winter swimming is cold. We know it's cold, and over time it becomes a normal cold, but it never becomes an easy cold. February and March are the coldest months as the sea heats up and cools down slowly. The coldest time is always the morning tide, especially on cloudless frosty mornings when the water has had time to run over the miles of frost and ice under open skies. It's pointless measuring the temperature – it's just very cold. Once we have changed, these morning swims go like this for me.

As I come down the steps, *sigh, sigh, sigh*. This is going to be cold so just let go. Practically now I would scoop some water into the hand and slap it onto the back of the neck. That's it, that's what's ahead of me – ready now.

What happens next is a kind of rapid hyperventilation which coordinates with the breath count frequency of 1:1, or even much less, and often corresponds with internal (and sometimes external) gasps of 'oh no, oh no', until, with time and acceptance, it all becomes 'ohh-kay'. This always accompanies a sigh. It's okay. It's finally okay. We are in and it's okay. We surrender to the cold.

We know from this experience that the breath of surrender and acceptance is a sigh because it is the breath the body unconsciously breathes to signal acceptance in the most extreme environment.

Breaths of Empowerment

Conscious breathing is a holistic practice. It is not really possible to put different breaths into separate categories of awakening, surrender and empowerment, but it's a useful model.

When we empower ourselves, we have the tools to lead. Our goal is to reach relaxed attention. This has been repeated a few times here because it is such an important concept. In a relaxed, attentive state we are here, we are relaxed and aware, whilst not reactive. This is the optimum state to be in when dealing with difficulties or emergencies. It's a bit like having access to our wisest self on speed-dial and hearing our voice say, 'You're okay, it's all okay, I know what to do.'

How reassuring is that?

Here are some breaths of empowerment that have helped me.

13. Coherent Breathing

This is one of the few breaths which has lots of empirical scientific evidence behind it. The lack of scientific evidence for the other breaths does not weaken them because with breathwork we become our own researcher and figure out what works for us. However, the data behind this one is very encouraging.

If you want to put your time and practice into just one additional breath, then I would suggest that box breathing or coherent breathing is a great place to start. In their book, *The Healing Power of the Breath*, Drs. Richard Brown and Patricia Gerbarg state:

> Coherent breathing is a simple way to increase heart rate variability (HRV) and balance the stress-response systems. When scientists tested people at all possible breathing rates, they found that there is an ideal breath rate for each person, somewhere between three and a half and six breaths per minute for adults using equal time for breathing in and breathing out, a sweet spot where the HRV is maximised and the electrical rhythms of the heart, lungs and brain become synchronised. Modern researchers have called this the resonance rate.[35]

Coherent breathing is about finding our resonance rate. This optimally balances the sympathetic nervous system (SNS) and parasympathetic nervous system (PNS) and stimulates heart rate variability. Drugs can suppress the SNS but there is nothing yet to boost the PNS.

There is evidence that coherent breathing does all of the above simultaneously in a drug-free way. For thousands of years, Chinese Medicine practitioners have used the pulse as a diagnostic tool to look for HRV among many other things. HRV is a measure of the time between heartbeats. Healthy people have greater HRV and stress adversely affects it.

The Heart Coherence 365 approach developed by Dr. David O'Hare disseminates this approach simply and is used as an example here.[36] There are a few key elements to this:

- Do it 3 times a day.
- Breathe at the rate of 6 breaths per minute.
- For 5 minutes each session.

Evidence shows that you will start to feel the benefits after ten to twelve days of regular practice and they will last for up to four hours between intervals. Space your sessions out through your day accordingly. There are some excellent videos on YouTube and a free app (RespiRelax+) is available to support you.

Earlier in the book I referred to being at the National Concert Hall and how I would use the breath to concentrate. During this time, I would practise coherent breathing, which for me immediately cuts through all jibber-jabber and keeps my attention in the present moment.

14. Box Breathing

This is the community breath that Navy SEALs practise while travelling or waiting together. Breathing together is unifying because of all the quiet and physical sharing of the breath that takes place. When it is coordinated the benefits are intensified.

Box breathing, like coherent breathing, is symmetrical and balanced. It adds two more components to the more rounded approach of coherent breathing. These are the pauses between the inhale and exhale and vice versa. Pausing here creates a conscious gap in the breath. Doing this opens a state of alert waiting. Breathing through the nose throughout is recommended.

A pattern initially of three seconds per side of the box is recommended, but with practice, this can be extended to four or five seconds. The pattern is:

·   Breathe in for three seconds through your nose.
·   Pause for three seconds on the inhale.
·   Breathe out for three seconds through your nose.
·   Pause for three seconds on the exhale.

The language too is important here. We are not holding our breath and creating tension in the system; we are simply pausing and observing a natural flow and being in that pause. As you breathe visualise tracing your fingers along the outside of the box with each count. As the practice of breathwork develops and internalises, it is possible to use the heartbeat as a count. This brings together heart and breath.

Box breathing, like coherent breathing, with regular practice creates relaxed attention. Both breaths reassure our chimp and safeguard us against reacting to things from this energy. If this empowers Navy SEALs, just imagine what it could do for you in your life.

15. Sufi Breathing

This is one of my favourite breaths. Sufism is the mystical body of Islam. This breath comes from that tradition. It is a type of breathing with predetermined numbers of inhales and exhales used throughout. The pattern is individual and needs to be established by the user. At all times, breathe through the nose. I prefer an asymmetrical pattern because this knocks me off balance and so makes me more conscious.

The breath also gives auditory feedback, especially when accompanied by the ujjayi placement of the tongue discussed earlier. When taking multiple inhales, try to breathe equally with each segment. So split over two breaths it might be: a half breath in plus another half breath in, and a full breath out. And then a full breath in with a half breath out plus another half breath out. It feels like going up a short step ladder two steps, then resting on the top for an exhale and inhale before stepping down the steps on the other side.

This is the breath combined with ujjayi breathing that was used when driving for hours in a thunderstorm. The asymmetrical pattern of it combined with an internal sound is like a buzz of attention keeping us alert.

Experiment and find your own pattern. Work out if a symmetrical or asymmetrical one is best for you. A symmetrical pattern will be balancing, like box breathing, whereas an asymmetrical pattern will unbalance and need you to stay more conscious to sustain it.

It can be a bit difficult to establish a pattern when Sufi breathing, as it is a counterintuitive breath. This is one of its strengths because it keeps us in the moment. It is quite intrusive, so it needs to be done at the right time. It works well as a standalone practice and is especially good when driving. It is a very good breath for awareness as it cuts straight through jibber-jabber and creates a relaxed and attentive state. It also helps me counteract fatigue. At work it would be a good breath to use if you wanted to empower yourself to be in an alert, watchful state.

16. Breathwalking

Guracharan Singh Khalsa and Yogi Bhajan came together to develop a programme which coordinates breathing and walking, and in this way, develop a dynamic walking yoga practice. Their book, *Breathwalk*, explains breathwalking in detail and includes many ancillary and supplementary activities.

Breathwalking is understood as a kind of internal metronome which coordinates the frequency of breath with the number of steps. Usually, two steps correspond to a count of one part of breath. The breath can be smooth throughout the walk or segmented in nature. The segmentation of a breath is exactly what is being done in a simpler way in Sufi breathing.

The basic walks are largely symmetrical in nature, with the in-breath and outbreath being the same length. Breath counts are taken from pranayama practice and are even to promote stability. Periods of non-breathwalking are interspersed with breathwalking for rest and focus. These are called vitality intervals.

The walker goes through an internal checklist before starting to ensure that they are correctly aligned; this is a bit like a vertical yoga nidra practice. Walking is seen as a dynamic as opposed to static yoga practice. There are tens of thousands of people who have trained in this programme worldwide.

In addition to the structured Breathwaking practices, it is good to be free with the breath as we walk. Using a short period of CCB while nasal breathing is good to experiment with. Additionally, both coherent and box Breathing are also good starting points to coordinate walking with the breath.

17. The 4-7-8 Breath

The 4-7-8 breath, also known as the relaxing breath, is a breathing pattern promoted by Dr Andrew Weil and draws its inspiration from pranayama practice.[37] It has been developed particularly as an awakening and anti-anxiety breath and often works well when used in the middle of the night if someone is having difficulty getting to sleep.

Lie on your back and use the ujjayi tongue positioning described earlier. Breathe in fully through the nose for a count of four. Pause the breath for a count of seven, then slowly exhale forcibly through the mouth, making a whoosh through pursed lips and feeling the circulation of the air due to the ujjayi tongue placement. In the 4-7-8 breath the inhale is quiet, and the exhale makes the exaggerated whooshing sound. Initially, due to the length of the hold and the exhale, it is recommended that just four rounds of this are practised initially, but these can be increased to eight breath cycles after a month or so of regular practice. After a while, the breath hold in the middle becomes easier and the length of one cycle of the breath can be extended.

In the same way as one conscious breath, this provides a gap to move us from reaction to response. It also helps with cravings. Dr Weil states that after two to three months of regular practice, there are significant physiological changes: it lowers heart rate, lowers blood pressure and improves digestion. He also says that the practice is a powerful anti-anxiety measure – much more powerful than anti-anxiety drugs commonly prescribed.

It is recommended to practise this at least twice daily, which is a time commitment of eight minutes. As this breath puts us into a state of deep relaxation, it is not recommended while driving.

18. Alternate Nostril Breathing

You can feel your nostril dominance at any point in time by closing opposing nostrils alternately and comparing airflow. Pranayama practitioners are taught that the right nostril energetically supplies the left hemisphere of the brain and the left nostril, the right one. The left side of the brain is broadly where language and rational thinking take place, and the right side is more where creativity and emotional responses arise. Generally speaking, the right nostril is associated with the SNS and the left nostril the PNS.

Every two hours or so the nostril dominance changes; this corresponds with the biorhythm which creates a shift between the left and right hemispheres of the brain. So we are shifting between being more creative and more linear every two hours or so. The transition point between the two is when we are in perfect balance, and most open and receptive. Interestingly, hypnotists are trained to watch the breath, as this is the ideal time to induce a trance.

This is a very relaxing and balanced breath. Use the thumb and ring finger of your preferred hand as this gives space to block the left and right nostrils. Start by exhaling, which empties the lungs. The alternate pattern for this is then, as follows:

- Inhale and exhale one breath through the left nostril.
- Inhale and exhale one breath through the right nostril.
- Practise alternate nostril breathing this way for ten minutes.

Now introduce one of the following counts:
- Inhale 4, pause 2, exhale 4, pause 2
- Inhale 4, hold 4, exhale 4, hold 4.

Swara yoga is an ancient tantric science that studies the breath flow through the nostrils (or *swara*) in relation to the phases of the moon and the time of day. It recommends changing nostril dominance at the first sign of physical, emotional or psychological imbalance. Here are some alternate nostril breathing uses they suggest:
- If you are feeling anxious or nervous, sit with a straight spine. Block the right nostril with the thumb of the right hand. Take 26 long deep breaths through the left nostril. Then inhale and relax.
- To reduce stress, close the right nostril. Inhale through the left nostril. Exhale through your mouth. Doing this for six minutes or so (roughly 28 breaths) quietens the mind.

There is a lot of evidence surrounding this practice within Indian philosophy. Play with it in a free and open way and build up your own experience and evidence.

Postscript

Dear Reader,

We have both reached the end. On the way together we have become breathers, walkers, and pilgrims. We have learned the most profound life lessons simply from our most vulnerable members: the neurodivergent children who inspired and taught me so much for many years.

Sometimes on the spiritual path we may have been too focused. You can see this in the people around you who set off in a frenzy of activity, focused on their goals, irrespective of what life throws at them. This is grasping. I did my fair share of this earlier. Don't worry, be realistic and flexible. Remember, in clearing your mind, life happens, and you have time and space to hear the messages of your heart.

When we slow we are more amenable to our flow. On the path you will meet both hares and tortoises. Don't overlook your inner tortoise as in a slow, plodding, purposeful way you will quietly, undramatically get there. You have time. Remember it only takes just one breath. I can write of this with some understanding as I set off as a hare in my twenties and hit many speedbumps on the way, but I got here, wherever here is, as a tortoise, and I remain a tortoise to this day, slowly raising my head for air.

Finally, before you re-enter the world at large, let's look back on the way we have come. We have seen that the breath is an extremely powerful portal which brings us to being and then, beyond that, to surrender. We know of other portals that will do a similar job, each a stepping stone to arrive in the present moment. This is a personal choice. I have come to see that the breath works most powerfully for me. That is why I have written about it. Try it for a few months and see if it works for you. Be free and find your own way.

Before finishing, in this final meditation, I want to offer you a way to follow the breath and let it lead you forward. It has been written for you from the heart of this book and draws on practices that have really supported me. I want this for you too.

◯ Let's breathe

Lie down or sit straight. I prefer to sit as the breath flows more naturally and can be experienced that way. Try and visualise an invisible thread from the top of your head to the ceiling, keeping it straight and aligned. We are now going to prepare the diaphragm in the same way that we did for the belly breathing exercise.

To do this, exhale. Take a large abdominal breath through your nose and count successive rounds of *1, 2, 3, 4, 5, 6, 7, 8, 9, 10* on the exhale. Rest for one breath between rounds and do two more cycles. This wakes up the diaphragm.

As the waves of the subsequent breaths calm and die down after this, just settle by taking natural flowing breaths in through the nose and out whichever way feels most comfortable. Don't introduce any pauses; keep the breath connected and rounded and smooth. Let the breath lead you and let the mind simply follow and observe. The breath is your teacher and guide and is an honest reflection of how you are and where you are. It leads you home to the wisdom of your heart. The mind's focus is to be busy and distractible. It has no role here other than to observe the breath and observe itself.

There is nothing to do but gently watch the breath. If a thought pops in, smile in gratitude to your mind for recognising it and let it drift off like a cloud across the sky. After this, return comfortably and happily to the breath. If a subtle and flattering thought about your practice pops up, smile in gratitude again; this is just your old friend, the ego, in disguise as a holy ego. Remember, we have rehomed that overzealous puppy and our heart is the boss of this relationship now.

Just watch the breath with gratitude. As you watch the breath, you may have a sense of the breath in the breath. That space within us is where we are being breathed. This usually flows from the diaphragm, which is why we started the practice by stimulating it. Don't look for this, but if you see it, smile quietly in stillness and gratitude.

Finish off by doing a round of five sighs. Try and do this for twenty minutes, twice a day. It is transformative.

Go now, pilgrim, be on your way.

'Weary Pilgrim' by Bob Quinn

Notes

1. Healthy Brains by Cleveland Clinic, 'You are your brain', https://healthy-brains.org/brain-facts/, accessed 7 Jun. 2024.
2. Mitchell, Damo, *A Comprehensive Guide to Daoist Nei Gong* (London, 2018).
3. Peters, Steve, *The Chimp Paradox: The Acclaimed Mind Management Programme to Help You Achieve Success, Confidence and Happiness* (London, 2012).
4. Svaldi, Jennifer, Griepenstroh, Julia, Tuschen-Caffier, Brunna & Ehring, Thomas, "Emotion regulation deficits in eating disorders: A marker of eating pathology or general psychopathology?" Psychiatry Research, 197(1-2) (2012), 103-111. doi: 10.1016/j.psychres.2011.11.009
5. Oremus, Will, 'Addiction for fun and profit', Slate (2017) https://slate.com/technology/2017/11/facebook-was-designed-to-be-addictive-does-that-make-it-evil.html, accessed 7 Jun. 2024.
6. Tolle, Eckhart 'The Greatest Liberation', [video] EckhartTolle.Com, https://eckharttolle.com/the-greatest-liberation/, accessed 3 Aug. 2024.
7. Krishnamurti Foundation Trust, 'Krishnamurti's Biography', https://kfoundation.org/krishnamurti-biography/, accessed on 3 Aug. 2024.
8. Thich Nhat Hahn, *The Miracle of Mindfulness* (1975).
9. The Two Norries Podcast, 'Podcast #1. Timmy's Journey.' [video], YouTube (uploaded 29 Jun. 2020), https://www.youtube.com/watch?v=0tF1EwgObZI, accessed 6 Jun. 2024.

10. Dalai Lama, 'A human approach to world peace', His Holiness The 14th Dalia Lama of Tibet, https://www.dalailama.com/messages/world-peace/a-human-approach-to-world-peace, accessed 5 Jun. 2024.

11. Wright, Robert, *Why Buddhism is True* (New York, 2017).

12. Maté, Gabor, *The Myth of Normal* (London, 2022).

13. Easwaran, Eknath, *The Bhagavad Gita for Daily Living* (2001).

14. Minford, John (tr.), *Tao Te Ching: The Essential Translation of the Ancient Chinese Book of the Tao* (2018).

15. These words (or similar) are said to have been uttered by Pope John XXIII at the end of every bedtime prayer.

16. Churchill, Winston, 'We shall fight on the beaches.' [speech] (1940).

17. Minford, John (tr.), *Tao Te Ching: The Essential Translation of the Ancient Chinese Book of the Tao* (2018).

18. Brown, Rita Mae, *Sudden Death* (1983).

19. Dass, Ram, *Be Here Now* (1971).

20. Campbell, Joseph, *The Hero's Journey: Joseph Campbell on His Life and Work* (New York 1990).

21. Rosen, Michael, *We're Going on a Bear Hunt* (Sydney, 1993).

22. Mingyur Rinpoche, Yongey, *In Love with the World* (New York, 2019).

23. Tolle, Eckhart, *A New Earth* (2005).

24. World Health Organization, Mental Health and COVID-19. Early evidence of the pandemic's impact (WHO, March 2022), https://www.who.int/publications/i/item/WHO-2019-nCoV-Sci_Brief-Mental_health-2022.1, accessed 3 Aug. 2024.

25. Kaufer, Katrin and Sharmer, Otto, *Leading for the Emerging Future: From Ego-System to Eco-System Economies* (San Francisco, 2018).

26. Hall, Becky, *The Art of Enough: 7 Ways to Build a Balanced Life and Flourishing World* (Great Britain, 2021).

27. Brulé, Dan, *Just Breathe* (2018).

28. Krishnamurti, J., *Total Freedom: The Essential Krishnamurti* (1996).

29. Green, Glenda, *Love Without End* (1999).

30. Dass, Ram, *Becoming Nobody* (2019).

31. Ephesians 6:10, Paul in his letter to the Ephesians.

32. Kornfield, Jack, *After the Ecstasy, the Laundry* (2001).

33. Krishnamurti, J., *Total Freedom: The Essential Krishnamurti* (1996).

34. The Physical Activity Guidelines for Americans. 2nd edition 2018. US Department of Health and Human Services

35. Massey, Heather, 'Cold-water swimming and why it is good for us to challenge our bodies.' The Physiological Society blog (7 Apr. 2022), https://www.physoc.org/blog/cold-water-swimming-and-why-is-it-good-for-us-to-challenge-our-bodies/, accessed 7 Aug. 2024.

36. Brown, Richard and Gerbarg, Patricia, *The Healing Power of the Breath* (2012).

37. O'Hare, David, *Heart Coherence 365: A Guide to Long Lasting Heart Coherence* (2014).

38. Weil, Andrew, 'Breathing exercises: 4-7-8 Breath' [video], Andrew Weil, M.D., n.d., https://www.drweil.com/videos-features/videos/breathing-exercises-4-7-8-breath/, accessed 12 Aug. 2024.

Selected Bibliography and Further Reading

Anderson-Lopez, Kristen and Lopez, Robert, 'Let It Go' [song] (2012).

Campbell, Joseph, *The Hero's Journey: Joseph Campbell on His Life and Work* (New York 1990).

Chopra, Melika, *Living with Intent* (2015).

Dostoevsky, Fyodor, 'Winter Notes on Summer Impressions' (1863).

Eknath, Easwaran, *The Bhagavad Gita for Daily Living* (2001).

Eckhart Tolle [website], https://eckharttolle.com/, accessed 3 Aug. 2024.

Green, Glenda, *Love Without End* (1999)

Gurucharan Singh Khalsa and Yogi Bhajan, *Breathwalk: Breathing Your Way to a Revitalized Body, Mind and Spirit*, (New York, 2000).

Kornfield, Jack, *After the Ecstasy, the Laundry* (2001).

Krishnamurti, J., *Total Freedom: The Essential Krishnamurti* (1996)

Logue, Christopher, 'Come to the Edge.' (London, 1969)

May, Rollo, *Freedom and Destiny* (1981).

Mehrabin, Albert, *Non Verbal Communication* (1972).

Minford, John (tr.), *Tao Te Ching: The Essential Translation of the Ancient Chinese Book of the Tao* (2019).

Mingyur Rinpoche, Yongey, *In Love with the World* (New York, 2019).

Vaknin, Sam, *Malignant Self-love: Narcissism Revisited* (2015).

About the Author

Michael Wood has recently moved on from his job as principal of a school for children with autism and complex behaviours. The children he worked with have been a great inspiration – although they were the pupils, he and his colleagues did most of the learning.

Michael worked with neurodivergent and deaf children in Ireland for nearly thirty years and earlier had a career in marketing in London. During the transition from one career to the other, he spent a year in India travelling and at Saccidananda Ashram in Tamil Nadu.

More recently he built a house and created a garden in the Slieve Bloom Mountains, where he held some retreats. He also became a spiritual companion with Anamcharadas in Dublin, trained online with Eckhart Tolle in the School of Awakening and more latterly in breathwork with Dr. Jim Morningstar in Transformations USA.

Michael is a keen pilgrim of the way of St James and works in the Dublin Camino Centre, where he meets fellow pilgrims, while talking about and dreaming of further Caminos.

He lives in Dublin with his partner and their son, and draws on his life throughout his writing. He is a keen gardener, cook and walker. This is his first book.

Milton Keynes UK
Ingram Content Group UK Ltd.
UKHW031909241024
449974UK00002B/9

9 781068 746604